Wavelength

Intermediate•Workbook

Gerald
Kelly

with
Ana Fraile
and
Alejandro
Zarzalejos

Longman

Contents

	Page
Introduction	v
Unit 1	2
Unit 2	7
Unit 3	12
Extend your reading: Units 1–3	19
Extend your grammar: Units 1–3	21
Extend your writing: Units 1–3	22
Unit 4	23
Unit 5	28
Unit 6	33
Extend your reading: Units 4–6	40
Extend your grammar: Units 4–6	42
Extend your writing: Units 4–6	43

	Page
Unit 7	44
Unit 8	49
Unit 9	54
Extend your reading: Units 7–9	61
Extend your grammar: Units 7–9	63
Extend your writing: Units 7–9	64
Unit 10	65
Unit 11	70
Unit 12	75
Extend your reading: Units 10–12	82
Extend your grammar: Units 10–12	84
Extend your writing: Units 10–12	85
Answer key	87

Introduction

Welcome to the **Wavelength Intermediate Workbook**. This Workbook and the Workbook Cassette/CD are designed to be used for individual study. The twelve Workbook units correspond to the twelve Coursebook units, reinforcing and giving further practice of the structures and language you have studied in class. Like the Coursebook, the Workbook has a strong emphasis on natural language, set in context, and texts with a human interest element. The Workbook provides you with a variety of activities to practise structure, reading, writing, listening and pronunciation. At the end of every three units the *Do you remember?* pages help you to review and re-activate the language you have learned in those units. The tapescripts for all the listening exercises can be found in the *Answer Key* at the back of the Workbook.

A special feature of this Workbook is that you will find extra pages of extended practice. These pages are optional, but are designed for students who would like more challenging practice in reading and writing skills, or in the structures they have studied in the Coursebook. This extended practice takes the form of following three sections:

Extend your reading

These sections come after every *three* units of the Workbook. They reflect the themes of the Coursebook units, but take a new look at them, use challenging texts, and include new vocabulary and exercises to develop your reading skills.

Extend your grammar

If you want more grammar practice there are special sections after every *three* units of the Workbook which include gap-fill exercises, practice in sentence transformation and use of tenses.

Extend your writing

The extended writing sections also come after every *three* units of the Workbook and cover different types of writing activities such as reports, e-mails, and formal and informal letters. Clear models are given as well as tips to help you organise your writing.

1 It takes all sorts

Adjectives

1 Fill in the gaps with words from the Word Box.

> chatty✓   stupid   boring   friendly   weird
> intelligent   nasty   upset

1 Our boss enjoys having a conversation.
He's really ....*chatty*.. .

2 But he looks miserable today.
He might be .... about something.

3 June's not very clever. She's a bit ....

4 June said something horrible about Trevor.
It was very ....

5 It's very easy to get on with Trevor.
He's so ....

6 Yes, but he's a bit .... He keeps
a photo of his pet snake on his desk. Very strange!

7 Julie's a very interesting woman.
She isn't at all ....

8 Erica's a very .... woman.
She's got a degree in biochemistry.

Present Perfect or Past Simple?

2 Make sentences about Dave and Sheila's travel experiences. Use the Past Simple or Present Perfect.

Examples: Sheila / Australia / 1999
Sheila went to Australia in 1999.
Dave / South Africa / Sheila
Dave's been to South Africa, but Sheila hasn't.

1 Sheila / Dave / Australia / 1999
Both ....

2 Dave / Sheila / Poland
Both ....

3 Dave / Sheila / Morocco / the same year
....
....

4 Dave / Argentina / India
.... and ....

5 Sheila / Russia / South Africa
.... but ....

6 Sheila / Russia / Dave
.... but ....

7 Sheila / India / Dave
.... the year before ....

2

Questions and answers

3 Write questions and short answers about Dave and Sheila. Use the passport information from Exercise 2.

Examples: Dave / Russia?

    Has Dave ever been to Russia?

    No, he hasn't.

    Did Sheila and Dave both go to the USA in the same year?

    Yes, they did .

1 Dave / Poland?

.... ?

Yes, he has.

2 Has Sheila ever been to South Africa?

....

3 Dave / go to India / 1997?

.... ?

No, he didn't.

4 Have Dave and Sheila ever been to Ireland?

....

5 Dave / Sheila / Argentina?

.... both .... ?

Yes, they have.

6 Did Sheila and Dave go to Argentina in the same year?

....

Pronunciation: questions and answers

4 **a)** Underline the stressed words / syllables in each sentence or question before you listen.

Example: Have you <u>e</u>ver been to <u>I</u>ndia? <u>Yes</u>, I <u>have</u>.

1 Have you ever been to Poland? Yes, I have.

2 When did you go? Two years ago.

3 Have you travelled much? Yes, I have.

4 When did you go to Japan? About three months ago.

5 Where did you go on holiday? I went to Kenya.

6 When were you there? A year ago.

b) 👓 (1) Now listen and check.

c) Draw an arrow on the last stressed syllable in each question and answer in Exercise 4a) to say if the intonation goes up ↗ or down ↘ at the end.

Example: Have you ever been to I↗ndia? Yes↘, I have.

d) 👓 (1) Now listen and check.

Listening: "Le Mange Tout"

5 **a)** 👓 (2) Dave and Sheila are travelling separately, but they meet in Hong Kong. Listen to their conversation. Are these sentences true (T) or false (F)? Write *T* or *F* in the boxes.

1 Dave and Sheila have met before. ☐
2 Dave has been to Tangier. ☐
3 Sheila has been to Rabat. ☐
4 Dave was in Morocco with some friends. ☐
5 Sheila thought Dave was nice. ☐
6 The restaurant "Le Mange Tout" is in Rabat. ☐
7 Sheila feels embarrassed. ☐
8 Dave's appearance has changed. ☐

b) Fill in the gaps in Dave's diary with the words from the Word Box. Use the Present Perfect or Past Simple forms of the verbs.

> go   visit   tell   eat   embarrassed
> meet (x 3)   to be   romantic   make up
> boring   upset   friendly (x 2)

Saturday June 23rd

Yesterday I .... (1) a really .... (2) girl, called Sheila. We .... (3) each other before, but I didn't realise at first! She told me a story about when she .... (4) in Morocco, with her friend, Trudi. Trudi started talking to a guy on the train (it was me!), and they thought I was really .... (5)! So, they decided to play a trick on us (I was with Pete and Julian). They .... (6) the name of a restaurant in Rabat, "Le Mange Tout", and arranged to .... (7) us there. Of course, it didn't exist, and they didn't intend to meet us anyway. It was just a trick. We spent a long time looking for that place! I remember being quite .... (8) at the time, as they seemed really .... (9). Anyway, I .... (10) her yesterday that we didn't look for it at all! She was really .... (11) when she realised it was me!

What a coincidence! We got on really well yesterday. We .... (12) to Kowloon Park together, and we .... (13) Cheung Chau island. We .... (14) a Chinese meal on the waterfront. It was really .... (15). We're going to meet again tomorrow at a café in Wanchai. I hope she turns up!

Alvin and Marcie

6 a) Alvin and Marcie Parsley are married. Circle the correct form of the verbs and *for / since*.

"I met Marcie when I was singing at a club in Birmingham. We**'ve known / knew**[1] each other **since / for**[2] 30 years or more. I **was / 've been**[3] a professional singer **for / since**[4] I was 18 years old, and Marcie **was / 's been**[5] my manager **since / for**[6] 28 years. We **'ve got married / got married**[7] on my 20th birthday. I **loved / 've loved**[8] Marcie **for / since**[9] the day we met. We **had / 've had**[10] a few problems over the years, but basically we love each other."

b) Fill in the gaps with the correct form of the verb or *for / since*.

"I (know) ....[1] Alvin since I (go) ....[2] to a club in Birmingham, on my 18th birthday. He (sing) ....[3] a song for me, but then he (fall) ....[4] off the stage! He (have) ....[5] a bad back ....[6] then. I (love) ....[7] him at first, but I (not love) ....[8] him for a long time now, not ....[9] he had an affair with Rita from our local shop. I (try) ....[10] to love him, and we have to work together – I (become) ....[11] his manager a long time ago – but we (be) ....[12] more like friends ....[13] the last five years or so."

c) Are these sentences true (T) or false (F)? Write *T* or *F* in the boxes.

1 Alvin is a professional singer. ☐
2 Marcie was Alvin's manager, but she isn't now. ☐
3 Alvin loves Marcie. ☐

4 Alvin has a bad back. ☐
5 Marcie loves Alvin. ☐
6 Alvin is having an affair with Rita. ☐

d) Alvin used to be a famous singer. He still sings, but sometimes he forgets the words. Fill in the gaps in Alvin's song, *Crazy, mixed-up guy*, with words from the Word Box.

| my best friend | depend | a life of my own | three hours | alone | since I met you |
| | boring | nothing in common | crazy | get on | |

We had ....[1], baby
But I could always ....[2] on you
And though I've got ....[3]
I'm sad that I've lost you.

We didn't really ....[4], baby
Will my loneliness never end?
And now you've gone, I'm all ....[5]
You ran away with ....[6].

I've loved you ....[7], baby
Though that was only ....[8] ago
You called me strange, desperate and ....[9]
Well, now I'm miserable also.

I guess I'm just a ....[10], mixed-up guy.

e) 🔊 (3) Now listen and check.

Opposite adjectives

7 Alvin's wife, Marcie is comparing Alvin with her idea of the perfect man. Decide which adjectives are positive, and which are negative, and put them in the correct columns. Look at the examples.

> self-confident✓ lazy impatient generous shy sociable two-faced mean insecure✓ sensitive sincere hard-working outgoing unsociable insensitive patient

Marcie's perfect man	Alvin
self-confident	insecure

Used to / would + infinitive

8 **a)** Fill in the gaps using *used to* and verbs from the Word Box.

> have✓ do feel sleep have go out be buy

Phil's life has changed a lot since he got married to Angela. He ....*used to have*.... a lot of free time, and he ....(1) most evenings. Now he's very busy and he stays at home, because he has so much to do. He feels moody a lot of the time, but before, he ....(2) cheerful most of the time. He ....(3) very well, but these days he is tired a lot of the time. He ....(4) a lot of exercise, too, but these days he feels really unfit. He has a lot of bills to pay; he ....(5) lots of money to spend, and he ....(6) Angela flowers every day. The strange thing is that since Philippa was born, he has become a lot more ambitious; he ....(7) happy with his job, but now he needs to earn more money!

Look at the passage about Phil again. In which gaps can you use *would*?

b) Write some sentences to say how *your* life has changed.

My life has changed since .... I used to .... but now ....

Before ....

....

....

Reading: Personalities

9 **a)** Write the situations (1–6) below in the spaces provided on the personality quiz from a magazine.

1 You are waiting for a bus. It hasn't arrived after fifteen minutes.

2 Which of these describes how you spend your free time?

3 Which of these describes you at work?

4 A friend has just split up with their partner.

5 It's your first day on a new course. You go to the coffee bar, and there are lots of people chatting.

6 You have been invited to a party, where there are lots of people who you've never met before.

Are you totally balanced?

Famous psychologist and TV personality Claude Janus thinks that everybody has two sides to their personality. He says that we all have positive and negative qualities, and that we show different qualities at different times. However, some of us show more of our positive qualities, and some of us show more of our negative qualities. Try our fun quiz, and see how balanced your positive and negative qualities really are.

Q1 ☐ Do you
a) approach a group of people, introduce yourself, and start chatting?
b) get a coffee, sit down and feel uncomfortable because nobody talks to you?
c) get a coffee, sit down, and chat to someone sitting nearby?

Q2 ☐
a) You go out once or twice a week, but you like to have some time for yourself, too.
b) You go out almost every evening with friends. You spend a lot of time on the telephone, too.
c) You really enjoy staying at home and watching TV, or reading a book. You don't like it when people phone you in the evening.

Q3 ☐ Do you
a) take the opportunity to make lots of new friends?
b) talk to the people that you know, but not talk to anyone else?
c) talk to the people you know, and introduce yourself to one or two new people?

Q4 ☐
a) You work hard, and you take a break when it is necessary.
b) You never take a coffee break, and you often work during your lunch break, too.
c) You take as many breaks as you can, and you let other people do your work.

Q5 ☐ Do you
a) ask them to tell you all the details immediately?
b) let them talk about it when they want to?
c) offer sympathy, but don't ask for any details?

Q6 ☐ Do you
a) wait until it arrives, and ask the driver if there is a problem with the traffic?
b) read your newspaper and just wait?
c) walk up and down, looking at your watch, and complain to the other people waiting that you are going to be late for work?

b) What do you think the other answers show? Write a), b) or c) next to these adjectives. Look at the example.

1 self-confident *a*	not very confident *b*	balanced *c*
2 sociable	unsociable	balanced
3 outgoing	shy	balanced
4 hard-working	lazy	balanced
5 sensitive	insensitive	balanced
6 patient	impatient	balanced

c) What are you like? Read the key from the magazine article. Fill in the gaps with *first, second* or *third*.

Here's the key to your personality:

1 If most of your answers are in the .... column, then you probably don't have any friends. You need to examine your life carefully.

2 If most of your answers are in the .... column, then you are too perfect. Have you answered honestly?

3 If most of your answers are in the .... column, then you are also too perfect. Have you answered honestly?

4 Most people have a mixture of answers from all three columns. If you have answered the questions truthfully, and have a mixture of each, then you truly are a balanced person.

②In the city

City vocabulary

1 Complete the words (1–12) from the picture.

1 _a_e_e_t	5 _a_l_n_	9 _o_t _o_
2 _o_u_e_t	6 _o_f_o_	10 _r_f_i_l__h_
3 _a_p-_o_t	7 _u_l_i_g	11 _h_n__o_
4 _a_c_n_	8 _o_d _i_n	12 _k_s___p_r

Listening: Croydon

2 **a)** 🔾🔾 (4) Tim is from Croydon in South London (UK). He's visiting Croydon, Pennsylvania (USA). Listen to the conversation and fill in the gaps.

TIM: Excuse me, could you tell me how to get to the Metro Hotel?

AMERICAN: Sure. You go past this .... (1), as far as the .... (2).

TIM: Yes …

AMERICAN: Then turn right, and walk past a large .... (3), which has a .... (4) outside.

TIM: Yes …

AMERICAN: Then you turn left, and cross the street to the opposite .... (5).

TIM: Yes …

AMERICAN: Keep going, past the .... (6) entrance and you can't miss it.

TIM: Er … past the … er …

AMERICAN: Or, you could just take a .... (7).

TIM: Sorry, could you tell me again?

b) 🔾🔾 (5) Listen to Tim talking about Croydon, South London, and say if these sentences are true (T) or false (F). Write *T* or *F* in the boxes.

1 Tim thinks Croydon is an attractive place. ☐
2 Tim doesn't like living in Croydon. ☐
3 Croydon is a good place to go shopping. ☐
4 People from many different countries live in Croydon. ☐
5 A lot of tourists go to Croydon. ☐
6 Croydon is a very clean place. ☐
7 It's easy to eat out in Croydon. ☐
8 There's a lot of traffic in Croydon. ☐
9 There are a lot of places to go out. ☐
10 Transport is difficult in Croydon. ☐

Countable and uncountable nouns: *much / many / a lot*

3 Write positive (P) and negative (N) sentences using *much / many / a lot*.

Example: (shops P) There are a lot of shops.

1 (tourism N)

....

2 (cars P)

....

3 (noise N) .... at night.

4 (litter P) .... on the streets.

5 (nightclubs N)

....

6 (taxis P)

....

Present Simple and Present Continuous

4 a) Ana is from Switzerland, but she's studying in the UK. Read this essay she wrote for her homework, and underline four mistakes in the use of the Present Simple and Present Continuous. Make the necessary corrections.

Compare your life in your country with your life at the moment

 I come — I'm coming from Zurich, and I stay here in London for three weeks. I really like studying at the Camford School of English, and it's a nice change from working at the bank. I also like my three flatmates, though I miss my parents, who I live with.

My short stay here is very different from my life in Zurich! Normally I'm taking my car to work, and using public transport in London has been interesting. I don't often go out at home, except at the weekends, but here in London I've been to lots of nightclubs, and I'm going out a lot more. I'm having a lot of friends at home, but now I get to know some new ones. I'm a bit worried about food; my diet is generally very healthy in Switzerland, but here I'm eating a lot of fast food, and I'm putting on a lot of weight!

b) Read Exercise 4a) again. Which of these ideas show what Ana usually does? Which show what's happening now? Write *U* (usually) or *N* (now).

> live / Zurich U   study / London N   use / public transport   go out / a lot   eat / healthy food
> put on / weight   meet / new friends   stay at home / evenings   drive / work   share a flat / other students
> have / a lot of friends   live / parents   work / bank   study / language school

Write sentences to compare Ana's life in Switzerland with her life in London.

Example: (live / Zurich) She lives in Zurich, but now she's studying in London.

1 usually work / bank ....

2 live / parents ....

3 normally drive / work ....

4 most of the time / stay at home / evenings ....

5 generally / eat healthy food ....

Questions and answers

c) Write questions and short answers about Ana. Use the Present Simple or Present Continuous.

Example: live / Berne?   Does she live in Berne? No, she doesn't. She lives in Zurich.

1 study / Paris? ....?

4 usually take the bus / work? ....?

2 usually live / boyfriend? ....?

5 have / a lot of friends in Zurich? ....?

3 share a flat / other students? ....?

6 eat well / at the moment? ....?

Pronunciation: auxiliary verbs

5 a) Decide if the underlined words in these sentences have a strong or weak form. Write *S* (strong) or *W* (weak).

1 <u>Are</u> you studying English?

Yes, I <u>am</u>.

2 Ana <u>has</u> a lot of friends in Zurich.

3 Where <u>are</u> you going?

To the airport. My parents <u>are</u> coming to visit.

4 <u>Have</u> you ever been to Washington?

No, I <u>haven't</u>.

5 What <u>do</u> you <u>do</u>?

6 <u>Are</u> they coming to the party?

Yes, they <u>are</u>.

b) 🔘 (6) **Now listen and check.**

State verbs

6

Jorge is from Spain, but he's living in London at the moment. Put a cross (*X*) next to the incorrect sentences below (there are five). Write the correct versions below.

1 I'm having a great time here in London.
2 I'm thinking it's a wonderful city.
3 I'm having a job in a burger bar.
4 I'm really enjoying the job.
5 I'm working with an Italian woman who's coming from Bari.
6 She isn't understanding me when I speak English.
7 I think she's liking me.
8 I'm thinking of asking her to go to the cinema with me.

1 ....

2 ....

3 ....

4 ....

5 ....

Past Simple and Past Continuous

7 Fill in the gaps with the Present Simple or the Present Continuous of the verbs in brackets.

1 When I .... (get) to the airport, my parents .... (wait) for me.

2 I .... (meet) my wife when I .... (work) in a hospital. Now I work in a school.

3 I .... (want) to get a job in advertising, but I .... (not have) the right qualifications.

4 I .... (see) a man standing on the corner. He .... (wear) a dark coat and a big hat.

5 The phone .... (ring) when I .... (have) a bath.

6 I .... (lose) my wallet when I .... (shop) in Oxford Street.

7 I .... (wait) for the bus when I .... (see) them.

8 What .... (you / do) when you .... (see) the man standing on the corner?

Echo questions and statements

8 Write echo questions for these statements, or use the correct tense of the verb in the statement.

Examples: She's staying in London for three months. <u>*Is she?*</u>

I (go) .<u>*went*</u>. to Hong Kong last year. Did you?

1 He's working in a burger bar. ....?

2 I (live) .... in Ireland when I was a boy. Did you?

3 I was working in a hospital when I met my wife. ....?

4 London is quite a polluted city. ....?

5 You look like Bruce Willis. ....?

6 They usually (drive) .... to work. Do they?

7 He was standing at the bus stop when I saw him. ....?

8 He (be) .... my best friend when I was a child. Was he?

Reading: *Westway*

9 **a)** Read this article about *Westway*, a radio soap opera, which is broadcast regularly on the BBC World Service.

Westway is set in the <u>fictional</u> London postal <u>district</u> of W15 (the W means that it is in the west of the city), which is a lively, multicultural inner-city area. It is actually based on the real Shepherd's Bush / West Kensington area of London; the area has a <u>flyover</u> called "the Westway", from which the radio programme takes its name.

The programme is set in a health centre, managed by Jamshed Dastoor, one of the main characters. Other locations include the local pub, the Green Man, and a community centre. The storylines follow the lives of the staff, customers and clients of the main locations, as well as street-life in the surrounding area. There are two fifteen-minute programmes a week, and an '<u>omnibus</u>' edition on Saturdays.

Westway tries to present an honest picture of London life, and it doesn't avoid serious and sometimes controversial issues although there are plenty of happy times, too. Its listeners like the programme's treatment of true-to-life situations, whether these are to do with family relationships or social problems, though some older <u>expatriate</u> British listeners have said that London was never like that when they lived there!

The programme is very popular with listeners, and attracts large audiences from China to Canada. Most of the comments e-mailed to the programme's website are very positive. Many people listen to it in order to help them improve their English.

Meet the characters

Jamshed Dastoor
Jamshed is the manager of the health centre. Janet's parents had jobs in India at that time. They knew Jamshed's parents, and they looked after him. His parents died in religious riots in India. He has a strong character beneath his gentle exterior.

Janet Dastoor
Janet is a nurse at the health centre, and is married to Jamshed. She is a warm person, and is full of fun, but she sometimes loses her temper.

Dr Margaret Sampson
Margaret started the doctor's surgery which grew into the health centre. She is a very determined woman, who has coped with many difficulties in her life.

Dr David Boyce
A very charming man, David lives with his wife, Jane (another doctor) and their two children. David's been working at the health centre for several years.

Dr Joy Onwukwe
Joy is a very ambitious woman. She started working at the health centre more recently. Her parents still live in Nigeria, but Joy has spent most of her life in Britain.

Denny Hampton
Denny's father is the landlord of the Green Man. Denny once got into trouble with the police a long time ago, but he now runs the local community centre.

The website address for *Westway* is www.bbc.co.uk/worldservice/arts/features/westway/index.shtml

b) Are these statements true (T) or false (F)? Write *T* or *F* in the boxes.

1 Westway is a real district of London. ☐
2 All of the action takes place inside. ☐
3 The programme tries to deal with real-life issues. ☐
4 The programme doesn't deal with family life. ☐
5 Some British listeners who live abroad think London hasn't changed at all. ☐

c) Find underlined words in the main text which mean:

1 people from a country who now live abroad ....
2 not real ....
3 an area of a city ....
4 a road which is raised above the ground ....
5 a complete edition of the week's programmes ....

d) Circle the correct verb forms in these sentences about the characters in *Westway*.

1 Jamshed *is managing / manages* the health centre.

2 Janet sometimes *gets / is getting* angry.

3 Margaret *has had / was having* many difficulties in her life.

4 David and Jane *are having / have* two children.

5 Joy *used to live / was living* in Africa.

6 Denny *has been / used to be* in trouble with the police.

Listening: *Hot City Nights*

10 **a)** [oo] (7) **Listen to the opening of a story, *Hot City Nights*. Which of these short summaries is correct?**

1 Johnny Damone is in New Orleans. He meets a nice guy who plays in a jazz band.
2 Johnny Damone is in New Orleans. He meets a woman in a bar, and wakes up in a strange room.
3 Johnny Damone is in New Orleans. He plays in a jazz band and sleeps in the street.

b) [oo] (7) **Now listen again. Put these events in the correct order, from 1–9. The first one is done for you.**

Johnny saw the woman. She was standing in the doorway. ☐
Johnny couldn't see the woman. ☐
She ordered a dry Martini. ☐
Johnny followed the woman into the street. ☐
Johnny woke up in a strange room. ☐
The woman put something in Johnny's drink. ☐
Johnny told her she had beautiful eyes. ☐
Johnny was sitting in a bar. ☐1☐
The woman came into the bar. ☐

Past Simple and Past Continuous

c) **Circle the correct forms in these sentences.**

1 Johnny **had a drink** / **was having a drink** in a bar in New Orleans when she **walked** / **was walking** in.

2 She **was wearing** / **wore** a summer dress, although it **rained** / **was raining** outside.

3 She **was asking for** / **asked for** a dry Martini.

4 Johnny **was thinking** / **thought** she had beautiful eyes.

5 Johnny **was not knowing** / **didn't know** where he was when he woke up.

6 When he **was waking up** / **woke up** a band **played** / **was playing** in the street outside.

d) **Read this summary of part of the story. Fill in the gaps using the expressions in the Word Box.**

> it was   there were   there was (x 2)   they were

When Johnny woke up ....(1) a lot of noise in the street outside. ....(2) some musicians outside, and ....(3) playing jazz music. ....(4) a woman standing in the doorway. Johnny followed her outside, and ....(5) hot and sunny.

e) **Here is the last part of the story. Fill in the gaps using the correct form of the verbs in the Word Box.**

> hit   stand   follow   dance
> look   disappear   smoke

I walked along the street. It was Mardi Gras, and a lot of people ....(1) and singing. I saw a police officer, and I asked him where I was. He laughed, and said, "You're in Basin Street. And you should go easy on the beer. It's only noon." I kept on walking, but I felt nervous. I was sure that someone ....(2) me. I turned around suddenly. Two men ....(3) right behind me. They got out a map, and looked at it. I went over to them and asked them how to get to Jackson Square. They pretended not to understand me, and answered me in bad English. I kept on walking. When I turned around again, they were still behind me, but they ....(4) at a poster on a wall. I continued walking. Then I saw the woman again. She was standing against a wall. She ....(5) a cigarette. When she saw me, she ....(6) round a corner. I ran after her. Suddenly, from nowhere, someone shouted "Hey, Johnny … Johnny Damone". When I turned, someone ....(7) me over the head with the lid of a trashcan … I realised then that I had to leave town.

f) [oo] (8) **Now listen and check.**

③ When Saturday comes

My kind of place

1 Read the clues and fill in the crossword.

1 "Let's go outside. It's too hot and … in here!"

2 A place where you can get to know people easily.

3 "This restaurant has a very … atmosphere. It's really laid-back."

4 Intimate and friendly

5 "Sorry, I can't hear you. It's too … in here."

6 "Can you put your cigarette out? It's too … in here."

7 "There's a lot of room here. It's very … ."

8 "Everyone goes there. It's a really … place at the moment."

9 Very light, not dimly-lit

Now write a definition of the word in the grey boxes. ....

Defining relative clauses

2 a) Put the words in the right order to make sentences.

Example: that's / where / I / club / my / boyfriend / the / met   *That's the club where I met my boyfriend.*

1 the / man / dance / to / me / he's / who / I / wanted / if / asked ....

2 we're / meeting / last / week / we / ate / the / restaurant / at / where ....

....

3 which / the / song / you / like / I / heard. ....

4 brother / man / over / there / there's / a / your / who / looks / like ....

5 whose / daughter / she / is / the / street / your / woman / lives / in? ....

....

b) Look at the sentences you wrote for Exercise 2a). Tick (✓) the sentences in which it is possible to use *that*. Put a cross (✗) next to the sentence in which you can leave out the relative pronoun.

Non-defining relative clauses

3 Use the second sentence of each pair to make a non-defining relative clause.

Example: I met my boyfriend at a club. It plays really trendy music.
       The club, which plays really trendy music, is where I met my boyfriend.

1 Derek asked me if I wanted to dance. He's very handsome. ....

2 The restaurant is closed on Sundays. It serves wonderful English food. ....

3 The song is at the top of the charts. It's by the group "Six Pack". ....

4 My friend is an actor. He was in the film *Pass the Salt*. ....

5 The house is in Hill End Lane. I was born there. ....

First Conditional

4 **a)** Peter is thinking about going out for the evening. He is a bit of a pessimist. Put his thoughts in a logical order (1–5). Now write four sentences using the First Conditional to explain Peter's thoughts.

go out	1	1 If I go out, ...
not be able to get taxi home	☐	2 ....
get home late	☐	3 ....
spend all my money	☐	4 ....
have to walk	☐	

b) Match these possible situations (1–5) with their possible results (a–e).

Situation	Result
1 If I don't save up my money	a) you won't get rid of that cough.
2 If I don't apologise	b) I won't have enough for a holiday.
3 If you don't stop smoking	c) you'll put on weight.
4 If you don't stop eating cakes	d) I'll get angry.
5 If you don't stop doing that	e) she won't talk to me again.

Use the ideas above to write sentences starting with *Unless*.

1 Unless ....

2 Unless ....

3 Unless ....

4 Unless ....

5 Unless ....

Plans and intentions

5 Fill in the gaps using the words in the Word Box.

> am going to   unless   if   will   won't

1 I've decided that I .... stop smoking. I've got a terrible cough, and I think that .... I do, I .... never get rid of it.

2 I think I .... stop eating cakes. I've been putting on a lot of weight, and .... I don't, I think I .... just get bigger! Also, I .... start going to the gym. I need to exercise more.

3 I think I .... apologise to her. .... I don't, she probably .... talk to me again. Also, I .... buy her some flowers. .... I don't, she .... go out with me again.

Strong and base adjectives

6 **a)** Fill in the gaps with *very* or *absolutely*, and appropriate base or strong adjectives.

> hilarious   starving   nice   big
> brilliant   awful

1 A: That film was .... good.

B: Good? It was ....!

2 A: That show was .... funny.

B: Funny? It was ....!

3 A: This burger's ....

B: ....? It's .... enormous!

4 A: This chicken's ....

B: ....? It's .... delicious!

5 A: The coffee tastes ....

B: ....? It's .... disgusting!

6 A: I'm feeling hungry. How about you?

B: Hungry? I'm ....!

b) (9) Now listen and check.

Uses of the First Conditional

7 a) Read these letters to an "agony aunt" for a newspaper. Match the First Conditional uses (a–d) to the letters (1–4).

a) a promise ☐   b) a prediction ☐   c) a threat ☐   d) a warning ☐

"Dear Zeena"
Zeena gives a quick answer to your emotional problems

1 Dear Zeena
I'm 17, and soon I'm getting married to a 73-year-old millionaire. His friends are being really horrible, saying that I don't love him, and that I only want his money. In fact, I love him because he is interesting and kind. They're all saying that the marriage won't last. What should I do?

2 Dear Zeena
I'm a 23-year-old man, and I don't know what to do with my future. I'm not interested in working in an office, and I really want to travel. My mother says that I should find a proper job, or I won't be successful. What should I do? Also, my girlfriend wants to get married …

3 Dear Zeena
I'm a rich, old man, and I live alone. My girlfriend is 17. I know that she doesn't love me, and that she's only interested in my money. However, I just want companionship and someone to cuddle at night. I asked her to marry me, and said that I will make her a rich woman. Do you think this was a good idea?

4 Dear Zeena
I'm a 22-year-old woman. My boyfriend wants to travel around the world, but I just want to get married and have children. Recently I told him that getting married is the only thing I want … or he will never see me again. Have I done the right thing?

b) Write a sentence to explain the problems in each letter. Start each sentence with *If*.

1 I marry him / marriage not last

....

2 not find a proper job / not be successful

....

3 she / marry me / make her a rich woman

....

4 he / not marry me / never see me again

....

c) Match Zeena's replies to the letters in Exercise 7a). Write the numbers 1–4 in the boxes at the start of each reply. Fill in the gaps using the words in the Word Boxes.

know   love   try   be sad

a) ☐ True love is hard to find. At your age, it is even harder. If you love this person, you might find the happiness that is missing from your life. But I think that if you don't .... (1) her, you will .... (2). On the other hand, you won't .... (3) if you don't .... (4).

resent it and leave you   let him go

b) ☐ True love is a strange thing. It makes us do crazy things. If you try to make him stay, he will .... (5) anyway. So, although it might be hard, you should .... (6).

all end in tears   be honest

c) ☐ It is clear from your letter that you are only in love with money, and that the only interest is financial. You must .... (7) with him. If not, it will .... (8). I think that marrying him will make you unhappy, too.

what you want to do   miss a wonderful opportunity

d) ☐ You need to be honest with yourself. Don't .... (9). Then you will see what the world has to offer. Do .... (10), or you will regret it. Why not become an English Language teacher?

Listening: Going out

8 a) 👀 (10) **Listen to these radio advertisements. Match these names to the places.**

Name	Place
CineFactory	a restaurant
Luigi's	a nightclub
Club Tropicana	a pub
Emilia Centre	a theatre
O'Connor's	a cinema

Which three places are good for families?

....

....

....

b) 👀 (10) **Read these questions carefully. Now listen again, and answer the questions.**

1 Tick (✓) the things that the CineFactory has.

Family films ☐
Saturday morning children's cinema club ☐
Ten screens ☐
Cheap films on Saturdays ☐
Classic movies ☐
Late-night shows ☐
The latest Hollywood blockbusters ☐

2 The music at Club Tropicana is described as

....

3 The atmosphere at Club Tropicana is described as

....

4 Before 10 p.m., how much do two beers and a glass

of wine cost? ....

5 Why? ....

6 What is the title of the play at the Emilia Centre?

....

7 The play is suitable for children. True ☐ False ☐

8 What is the special offer at Luigi's? Tick one box.
All you can eat for £67. ☐
All you can eat for the price of one meal. ☐
All you can eat for the price of a beer. ☐

9 O'Connor's doesn't serve food. True ☐ False ☐

10 You can bring children to O'Connor's in the evening.
True ☐ False ☐

c) A restaurant critic wrote this passage about Luigi's. Fill in the gaps using the words in the Word Box and the correct form of the verbs.

good	excellent	busy	family
delicious	waiters	meal	dishes

Luigi's is the sort of place that should be kept secret, so that not too many people go there! The food is basic, but very ....(1). My ....(2) was served on time, and there is a wide choice of traditional Italian ....(3). The ....(4) were friendly and fun, and there is a great ....(5) atmosphere. There's also an ....(6) special offer at the moment. You can eat all you want for the price of one meal, but only on Fridays, from 6–7 p.m. There was a big queue when I went last Friday, and it was very ....(7). However, if you (feel) ....(8) like (have) ....(9) an absolutely ....(10) dinner, or if you simply (want) ....(11) (have) ....(12) a snack, you (like) ....(13) Luigi's.

d) 👀 (11) **Listen to this telephone complaint about *Pasta Disaster* at the Emilia Centre, and answer the questions.**

1 Tick (✓) one answer.
The woman …
liked the play, but not the theatre. ☐
liked the theatre, but not the play. ☐
didn't like the theatre or the play. ☐

2 Tick (✓) the boxes to say which problems the woman mentions.
it wasn't funny ☐
the acting was bad ☐
the theatre was cold ☐
the theatre was hot ☐
the theatre was dirty ☐
she didn't like the actors' hats ☐
the seats were small ☐
she couldn't see ☐

Listening: A good night out

Making suggestions

9 a) Fill in the gaps using the correct verb forms. For each gap, use a word or expression from both Word Boxes.

> feel like   don't want   let's
> should   'd like   why don't we

> have   go   do   go   eat out   do

BRENDAN: What do you ....(1) tonight?

ANN: We ....(2) somewhere special. It's your birthday!

BRENDAN: ....(3) at a restaurant.

ANN: No, I ....(4) to a restaurant. I ....(5) fun!

BRENDAN: But it's *my* birthday! ....(6) what *I* want to do?

b) 🔊 (12) **Listen to Ann and Brendan. Who likes what? Write *A* (Ann) and / or *B* (Brendan) next to these expressions.**

going to clubs ....
going for a curry ....
going to an Internet café ....
dancing ....
going home to watch a video ....
listening to music ....
going to a friend's house ....
going to pubs ....

c) Ann and Brendan are going out on the town. Fill in the gaps in their conversation using the words in the Word Box.

> relaxed   fashionable   delicious   spacious
> crowded   cosmopolitan   noisy   cosy

ANN: There's a really good bar near here.

BRENDAN: Really? What's it like?

ANN: The atmosphere's really calm and ....(1), and it doesn't get too ....(2). It's very ....(3), and you can always find somewhere to sit.

BRENDAN: What sort of people go there?

ANN: You get all sorts of different nationalities. It's very ....(4).

BRENDAN: What's it like inside?

ANN: It's comfortable and ....(5). There are small tables, and lots of armchairs. You can sit and read the newspaper. They serve food, too. I had a really ....(6) meal there once.

BRENDAN: What sort of music do they play?

ANN: Oh, there isn't any music. It isn't a ....(7) place. It's open until midnight. Do you want to go? Come on! Everyone goes there! It's very ....(8)!

BRENDAN: No. It doesn't sound like my kind of place.

d) 🔊 (13) **Now listen and check.**

Present Continuous: making arrangements

10 Peter is a busy man. Write sentences using the Present Continuous to explain why he and Dick can't make arrangements to meet.

> *Monday: Dentist 6.30*
> *Tuesday: Give presentation at work, 3 p.m.*
> *Wednesday: Do my washing – evening*
> *Thursday: Dinner with Chastity – evening*
> *Friday: Theatre with my parents*
> *Saturday p.m. – play golf with Tom*

DICK: So, Peter, when shall we meet up? How about Monday evening?

PETER: *Sorry, I can't. I'm going to the dentist.*

DICK: I'm free Tuesday afternoon.

PETER: ....(1)

DICK: Wednesday evening?

PETER: ....(2)

DICK: That's no excuse! How about Thursday evening?

PETER: ....(3)

DICK: Is Friday evening any good?

PETER: ....(4)

DICK: Saturday afternoon. Unless you're washing your hair that day!

PETER: ....(5)

Reading: London's theme restaurants

11 a) Read the newspaper article quickly, and fill in the gaps with the names of the restaurants.

Sarastro is the restaurant which has live classical music and opera.
The Hard Rock Café is the restaurant which is older than the others.
La Pergola is the restaurant where you can listen to the songs of a famous dead singer.
Babe Ruth's is the restaurant which is named after an American sporting hero.

Rock Music! Sport! Opera! Elvis! Food!

London has a lot of theme restaurants, which cater for many different tastes. Some celebrate music or famous sporting heroes, and there are others which have invented an original theme to entertain their customers. We visited some of London's favourites.

(1) ....
150 Old Park Lane, W1

This was London's first real theme restaurant, which opened in the 1970s. It made a big impression when it opened, because it was new and exciting, and also because the real American-style hamburgers were bigger and better than anything the British public had seen before. The restaurant is full of rock music memorabilia and the music is loud, and also quite old. If you remember the music, you will probably want them to turn it down! It is now part of a huge organisation with restaurants in many cities around the world, and the one in London is very popular with tourists. There is often a big queue outside, but waiting to get in is a part of the whole experience! You can also buy a T-shirt, to show you've been there!

(2) ....
126 Drury Lane, WC2

The restaurant is in the heart of London's theatre district, and owners call it "the show after the show". So, you can guess that people don't come here just to eat, they come to be entertained! The inside is like an opera house, and there is a 'Master of Ceremonies' to introduce the entertainment. On some evenings there is live opera, and on others there is Turkish classical music. If you go as a couple, you might get a table in one of the 'boxes' (just like in a theatre) halfway up the wall; the waiter has to climb a ladder to bring you your meal! The food is described as 'International', but there is a strong Turkish influence. The restaurant offers a great night out, and excellent entertainment.

(3) ....
172–176 The Highway, E1

This restaurant and bar is named after the American baseball player, who played mostly for the Boston Red Sox and New York Yankees in the 1920s and 1930s. The theme is sport, and the atmosphere is typically American. You don't have to eat, but the most popular meals on the menu are burgers, pizza and pasta, and you get an enormous portion! If you want to lose a little weight after eating, there is also a miniature basketball court!

(4) ....
66 Streatham High Road, SW16

This is not really a theme restaurant, but it offers you a restaurant experience with a difference. When you go in, you find an Italian restaurant, with an Italian atmosphere and a good Italian menu. However, if you go on a Friday or Saturday night, you will be entertained by Elvis Presley! Not by the real Elvis, of course, but by Kim Bridges, a singer born in London, who is probably the best Elvis impersonator around! Kim's show has become famous, and people travel a long way to see the show. Wonderful entertainment, and fantastic food!

b) Tick (✓) the best answer.

1 The Hard Rock Café was …
  a) London's first exciting restaurant. ☐
  b) the only exciting restaurant to open in London in the 1970s. ☐
  c) London's first theme restaurant, and it opened in the 1970s. ☐

2 Sarastro is probably called "the show after the show" because …
  a) people go there twice in the same evening. ☐
  b) people go there before they go to the theatre. ☐
  c) people go there after they have been to the theatre. ☐

3 People go to Sarastro for …
  a) the food only. ☐
  b) the food and the entertainment. ☐
  c) the entertainment only. ☐

4 At Babe Ruth's you …
  a) have to eat burgers, pizza or pasta. ☐
  b) can just have a drink, if you want to. ☐
  c) can't have a drink if you don't eat. ☐

5 La Pergola …
  a) has a special show on Fridays and Saturdays. ☐
  b) isn't open on Fridays or Saturdays. ☐
  c) is only open on Fridays and Saturdays. ☐

Do you remember? Units 1–3

Yes / no and *wh-* questions

1 a) Put the words in the right order to make questions, and match the answers (a–f) to the questions (1–6).

1 been / you / Paris / ever / have / to?   *Have you ever been to Paris?*   a) With my boss.

2 go / you / did / there / holiday / on?   ....   b) Yes, I did.

3 did / you / what / there / do?   ....   c) No, it was business.

4 go / when / you / did / there?   ....   d) Last year.

5 visit / you / any / did / monuments / famous?   ....   e) I went to lots of meetings.

6 with / go / you / who / did?   ....   f) Yes, I have.

b) Fill in the gaps using the Past Simple or Present Perfect form of the verbs in brackets.

I'll never forget the first time I (go) .... [1] parachuting. It (be) .... [2] the day

after my 21st birthday, and I (be) .... [3] really excited. We (do) .... [4] some

training the day before, and (learn) .... [5] how to jump and how not to hurt

ourselves. The next day, when we (get) .... [6] into the plane, I (feel) .... [7]

really nervous. As we (go) .... [8] higher, I (become) .... [9] a little frightened.

In fact, I don't think I (be) .... [10] so frightened in my life! Anyway, when it

(be) .... [11] my turn to jump, I (decide) .... [12] I (have to) .... [13] do it.

It (be) .... [14] fantastic! It (take) .... [15] about three minutes to come down,

and I really (enjoy) .... [16] it. I (do) .... [17] it about three times since then.

c) Fill in the gaps with question words. Match the answers (a–f) to the questions (1–6).

1 .... did you go parachuting?   a) Absolutely terrified!

2 .... did you go to do it.   b) Some friends.

3 .... did you feel?   c) Because I wanted to!

4 .... did you do it with?   d) About three minutes.

5 .... did you do it?   e) About ten years ago.

6 .... did it take to come down?   f) A place called Sibson.

Revision of verb forms

2 Fill in the gaps with the correct form of the verbs in brackets.

CUSTOMER: Waiter! There (be) .... [1] a fly in my soup!

WAITER: That (not be) .... [2] a fly, sir.

That (be) .... [3] the meat.

CUSTOMER: I'm afraid you are wrong. I want to know what

it (do) .... [4] there.

WAITER: I think it (swim) .... [5], sir.

CUSTOMER: I want (speak) .... [6] to the manager.

WAITER: OK, sir. I (get) .... [7] him for you.

MANAGER: Yes, sir. Can I (help) .... [8] you?

CUSTOMER: Yes. If you (not apologise) .... [9] for the

fly in my soup, I (not pay) .... [10] for

this meal!

MANAGER: I'm sorry, sir. Would you prefer a spider?

Extend your reading Units 1–3

1 Read the extract from *Don't Say Yes When You Want To Say No* and answer these questions.

1 What happens if you can't say no?

....

2 When should you say yes?

....

3 When is saying yes a bad idea?

....

People in our society always make requests or place demands on others. You must be able to stand up for yourself by the simple process of saying no. If you can't state this simple two-letter word when you want to say it, you begin to lose control of your life.

This does not mean saying no to everything. You say yes when you want to give an affirmative response. If doing a favour for a friend or participating in a community event may inconvenience you, there is nothing wrong with saying yes if you feel the matter is important enough. Saying yes becomes wrong when you want to say no and it is in your best interest to say no, but instead you end up with a feeble "OK, I'll do it."

The inability to say no has several consequences.

It leads you into activities you don't respect yourself for doing.

It distracts you from what you really want to accomplish. You become so burdened doing the things you don't want to do that you have neither time nor energy for the things that are most important.

Because you allow other people to exploit you continually, the resentments build up, and sometimes, after years of the yes routine, you lose your temper in an inappropriate outburst. If you always perform all kinds of errands for others at great inconvenience to yourself, eventually someone makes a trivial request and you explode. This stems not from the most recent incident, but from hundreds of occasions. What the yes-sayer doesn't realize is that this behaviour often creates lack of respect rather than liking.

It produces a lack of communication between you and others. Unless there is honest communication people cannot understand each other. Saying yes when you mean no is not the quality of sweetness and light; it is dishonest.

2 If you can't say no, then you will find yourself in these situations. Put them in the same order as in the extract. Number them 1–4.

a) You will feel angry because people are always asking you to do things. ☐

b) You will do things that you don't think are good. ☐

c) You won't tell other people your real thoughts and feelings. ☐

d) You won't have time to do what you really want to do. ☐

3 Read these examples of two of the situations (1–4). Match them to the situations.

a) For some thirty years, my wife Jean always said 'yes, I'll do it' to her friend Cathy. One day Jean made the first demand she had ever made of Cathy. Cathy's reply was, "Sorry, I'm just too busy." In the middle of the crowded restaurant, Jean lost her temper.
Situation: ☐

b) One patient complained to me because every Sunday afternoon her husband would ask, "Wouldn't you like to go to the movies?" She couldn't say no, so off they would go to the neighbourhood movie. Then one day she spoke up, "No, I don't like going to the movies on Sunday afternoon." Much to my patient's surprise, her husband said, "Why didn't you say so? I hate going to the movies on Sunday. I thought I was pleasing you."
Situation: ☐

4 Complete these definitions with these verbs from the extract.

> stand up for   end up   builds up
> lose your temper   stem from

1 When you .... , you get angry.

2 To .... in a situation means you get into it without meaning to.

3 If you .... somebody, you defend them.

4 When something .... , it increases.

5 If a situation .... something, it was caused by this thing.

5 Read the second extract from the same book. Match the headings (a–d) to steps 1–4.

a) Compare your answers with these answers. ☐
b) Think of some more requests to refuse. ☐
c) Say no to these two requests. ☐
d) Practise saying no in real life. ☐

You, too, can learn to say no. To start your personal training programme, do the following exercises.

Step One: Take each situation listed below and think of your answer to it. Write it down.

• *Situation One:* A colleague asks to borrow some coins for the office coffee machine. Somehow he always does this and never repays you. He says, "Would you lend me some change for the machine?" How do you say no?

• *Situation Two:* A friend had asked you to go with him 'sometime soon' to select a new hi-fi set. You had assented. On the Saturday morning when you had been planning to catch up with house chores, he calls and says, "You promised to help me pick out that hi-fi set. Can you come with me this morning?" How do you say no?

Step Two: After you have said no to the above situations in your way, read the following models and compare your answers to them. Then try the questions a second time. Remember, the answers you give do not have to do be exactly like the models, but you should follow their principles: brevity, clarity, firmness, honesty.

• *Situation One:* Colleague and the coffee machine

Models: "No, sorry, you owe me for too many coffees already."

"No, you never pay back."

Note: Each answer is short and does not explain at great length.

• *Situation Two:* The hi-fi set

Models: "No, I can't make it today. How about next Saturday?"

"I will go with you, but not today. I'm sorry."

Note: The answers recognise the commitment but also the bad timing.

Step Three: Practise saying no. Think of several unreasonable requests. Now imagine yourself saying no – firmly, and without overlong explanation.

Step Four: As a final step, look for opportunities to say no in life situations.

6 Are these statements true (T) or false (F)? Write *T* or *F* in the boxes.

1 In Situation One, you say no because you haven't got any money.

2 In Situation Two, you say no because you want to do something else.

3 In Situation Two, you promise to help your friend another time.

4 It's important to speak the truth when you say no.

5 It's important to explain fully why you are saying no.

7 Match the words (1–5) to their meanings (a–e).

A	B
1 select	a) clearness
2 assent	b) choose
3 brevity	c) certainty
4 clarity	d) shortness
5 firmness	e) agree

Extend your grammar Units 1–3

1 Fill in each gap in the text with one word from the Word Box. There are some words you won't need.

also	among	atmosphere	but	certain	compares	however	it	its	like	mix
only	purpose	reason	than	that	their	this	those	to	usage	with

Problems crossing the road, illegally parked cars and fears for personal safety are ....(1) the complaints from people visiting Dublin city centre, according ....(2) a report which compares the capital with other European cities. ....(3) a good number of both the visitors to the city and locals expressed how much they liked the ....(4) of activities and atmosphere in the city centre. Most people selected Grafton Street, Henry Street and Temple Bar as ....(5) favourite parts of the capital.

The report, "Streets As Living Space", is part of a European study and includes comments on lifestyle in Dublin city centre. ....(6) was prepared for the Dublin Transportation Office (DTO), and ....(7) Dublin with cities and towns in Northern Ireland, Britain, Germany, Italy and the Netherlands. It examines a range of factors ....(8) means of transport, ...(9) of visit, social activities, likes and dislikes of cities, problems for pedestrians, shopping behaviour, car parking and ....(10).

It ....(11) found the bus was the favourite means of transport for journeys to the city centre for shopping, leisure and personal reasons. Bus ....(12) was the third highest of the cities surveyed, with ....(13) Birmingham and Edinburgh having more people travelling by bus. In addition to ....(14), the proportion of people walking, 21 per cent, is also higher ....(15) the average for a city of Dublin's size. Half of ....(16) coming to the city were local, but 10 per cent had travelled distances of more than fifty miles.

............................(17), Dublin didn't score very high against ....(18) European competitors in a number of areas, including difficulty in crossing the road, problems ....(19) illegally parked cars and concerns about crime and personal safety. Some people said they also felt uncomfortable about a general air of decline in ....(20) neighbourhoods.

2 Complete the second sentence using the word in capitals so that it means the same as the first sentence.

Example: I saw Michael a minute ago.

JUST

I *have just seen* Michael.

1 When I was younger I used to go out more often.
WOULD
When I was younger ....
more often.

2 There were a lot of cars on the road to Liverpool.
TRAFFIC
There .... on the road to Liverpool.

3 Unless you leave at once, I'll call security.
DON'T
If .... I'll call security.

4 This café has been open for three months.
AGO
This café ....

5 Why not come and stay with us for a few days?
ABOUT
....with us
for a few days?

6 He doesn't work as a translator any more.
LONGER
He no .... translator.

7 I had to make only three phone calls during my holiday.
WHILE
I had to make only three phone calls ....
.... holiday.

8 He used to be very impatient but he is not now.
BECOME
He .... patient.

Extend your writing Units 1–3

1 Look at this e-mail from Emma Hart, a single woman who lives in a flat in London, to some friends in New York. The style in which it is written is too formal for contact with a friend. Replace the underlined formal words / phrases in the five paragraphs of the e-mail with these more informal ones and rewrite the e-mail.

Paragraph 1
the flat where I live   you and Tom
'cos   I've got to   thanks   at last
I won't be able to make it   a few
great   haven't been in touch   tell
I feel as though   sorry   sort it all out

Paragraph 2
hasn't got a job   fridge   bad
we haven't got very much   thing
I can't   It turned out   The other day
I've never got on   really   nicking
one weird guy   that I thought was
I think   shouted at him for   stay

Paragraph 3
sort things out   So that's why   come to
A friend of a friend   I've got to
has offered me a place on her floor
I can't   a few days   a.s.a.p.

Paragraph 4
Sorry again   Get in touch   get together
photos   when you get back
I can't wait to see   fix a time

Paragraph 5
All the best to you both

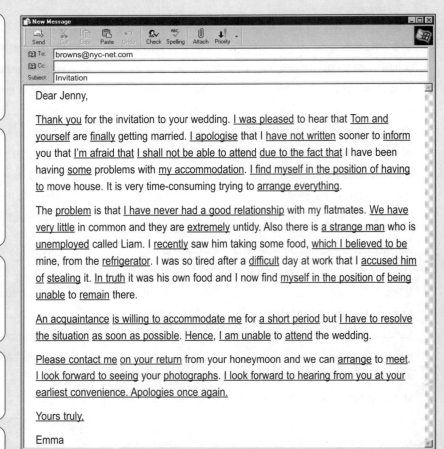

New Message

To: browns@nyc-net.com
Cc:
Subject: Invitation

Dear Jenny,

Thank you for the invitation to your wedding. I was pleased to hear that Tom and yourself are finally getting married. I apologise that I have not written sooner to inform you that I'm afraid that I shall not be able to attend due to the fact that I have been having some problems with my accommodation. I find myself in the position of having to move house. It is very time-consuming trying to arrange everything.

The problem is that I have never had a good relationship with my flatmates. We have very little in common and they are extremely untidy. Also there is a strange man who is unemployed called Liam. I recently saw him taking some food, which I believed to be mine, from the refrigerator. I was so tired after a difficult day at work that I accused him of stealing it. In truth it was his own food and I now find myself in the position of being unable to remain there.

An acquaintance is willing to accommodate me for a short period but I have to resolve the situation as soon as possible. Hence, I am unable to attend the wedding.

Please contact me on your return from your honeymoon and we can arrange to meet. I look forward to seeing your photographs. I look forward to hearing from you at your earliest convenience. Apologies once again.

Yours truly,

Emma

2 a) Emma is trying to find a flat. Read this e-mail from her estate agent.

New Message

To: emma@online.co.uk
Subject: Flat

Dear Ms Hart,

Thank you for your enquiry concerning the flat at 37 Freedale Road.

I have spoken to the landlord and I am pleased to inform you that there is a room available which we could view together at 10 a.m. this coming Thursday morning.

Would you be kind enough to reply to this e-mail as soon as possible so that I can contact the landlord and confirm the appointment?

Yours sincerely,

Laura Swinburne.

b) These are the notes that Emma made to write a reply to the estate agent. Write her reply e-mail in a formal style.

Great / get e-mail saying appointment sorted out / see flat.

Sorry not in touch sooner. Couldn't 'cos only just back from business trip.

Sorry but can't make it on Thursday / car problems / Friend can drive me on Weds / is that possible/ want to fix it up for then.

Hope OK / want new flat a.s.a.p.

Hear from you soon. Sorry again that can't make it.

Yours

4 How do you do that?

Skills and abilities

Glen
Glenda
Arthur
Martha

1

Name:		
Subject	**Comments**	**Position in Class**
Maths	(a)	1
English	Average work. Could do better.	15
French	(b)	30
Science	Good work. Making good progress.	10
Sports	Not really a sporty child, though he tries hard.	25

2

Name:		
Subject	**Comments**	**Position in Class**
Maths	Making good progress.	8
English	She tries hard, but has some difficulty writing essays.	23
French	Average ability. Has made progress, but could do better.	13
Science	(c)	1
Sports	(d)	30

3

Name:		
Subject	**Comments**	**Position in Class**
Maths	(e)	30
English	(f)	1
French	Very good work, and making good progress.	9
Science	Tries hard, though she finds it difficult.	24
Sports	Average ability.	15

4

Name:		
Subject	**Comments**	**Position in Class**
Maths	He finds this subject difficult, although he tries hard.	23
English	(g)	30
French	(h)	1
Science	Average ability, but he could do better.	13
Sports	Quite good at sport. Doing very well.	7

1 **a)** These are school report cards for the children in the pictures. Write the children's names on their reports.

b) Look at the pictures and put this information into the correct places on the report cards.

1 She is an extremely good scientist, and understands everything.
2 She isn't interested in sports. She tries to catch the ball when playing tennis.
3 His French is extremely good, so it is a surprise that his work in this subject is so bad.
4 This is her worst subject. Can't add 2 + 2.
5 Extremely good work. Her work on Shakespeare was brilliant.
6 He is nearly fluent. Extremely good work this year.
7 Extremely good work this year.
8 He shows no interest in this subject.

> extremely good   quite good   good
> hopeless   not very good

c) Fill in the gaps in the sentences. Look at the marks and comments on the report cards.

Example: Arthur is extremely good at maths.

1 Martha .... English.

2 Glen .... science.

3 Glenda .... sports.

4 Arthur .... English.

5 Martha .... science.

6 Glen .... French.

7 Glenda .... English.

Reading: The right dog for the job

2 **a)** Read the text and match the pictures (a–e) with the descriptions (1–5).

a) German Shepherd   b) Poodle   c) Golden Retriever   d) Great Dane   e) St Bernard

Dogs and people have lived and worked together since the early days of human existence. People found that domesticated dogs made extremely good companions. They also found that dogs could be trained to perform particular tasks. People noticed the characteristics of dogs which they found useful, and over a long time, began to develop different breeds of dogs for different tasks. Here are some well-known breeds, and the reasons why people have found them useful.

1 ☐ These dogs were originally trained to protect sheep from wild animals, because they are naturally aggressive. When properly trained, they are docile dogs, and they are used by police in many countries.

2 ☐ This huge dog is mostly associated with Switzerland. All dogs have a very good sense of smell, but this breed's is better than most. It also has an extremely good sense of direction, and these two qualities combined mean that the dog can easily find people who are lost or trapped in snow.

Although these days people prefer to rely on modern technology, they are still used in some remote areas.

3 ☐ Although their name suggests that they come from Denmark, these enormous dogs were originally bred in Germany, and were used to guard the entrance to castles. Today they are mostly kept as pets (they are good with children), guard dogs and as show dogs.

4 ☐ These dogs are good at fetching things. They were originally used for hunting, especially to fetch birds which had been shot. They became popular in Britain in the 1800s, they have a terrific sense of smell, and they can also swim very well.

5 ☐ Today most people don't realise that these dogs were once used for hunting. They are excellent swimmers, and their owners used to cut their fur in order to help them swim better. The way that they are 'clipped' these days is a very exaggerated version of the original style. They are mostly used these days as show dogs and pets.

b) Underline words or expressions in the text which mean the same as the following.

a) trained to live with people
b) natural features and abilities (x 2)
c) tasks
d) types (e.g. German Shepherd)
e) calm

f) very big (x 2)
g) go somewhere and bring something back
h) killing animals for food or sport
i) very good (x 2)
j) an animal's 'hair'

c) Choose two correct answers for each statement.

1 Dogs are good at …
   a) working with people. ☐
   b) performing any task. ☐
   c) living with people. ☐

2 German Shepherds are good at …
   a) stopping sheep from attacking wild animals. ☐
   b) stopping wild animals from attacking sheep. ☐
   c) being aggressive. ☐

3 St Bernards are good at …
   a) finding people lost in snow. ☐
   b) finding their way. ☐
   c) using modern technology. ☐

4 Great Danes are good at …
   a) guarding property. ☐
   b) looking after animals. ☐
   c) playing with children. ☐

5 Golden Retrievers are good at …
   a) swimming. ☐
   b) getting and bringing back animals. ☐
   c) shooting birds. ☐

6 Poodles are good at …
   a) fishing. ☐
   b) hunting. ☐
   c) swimming. ☐

Listening: New tricks

3 a) (14) **Pat is 65 years old. Listen to her talking about things she has learned to do in her life. Are these sentences true (T) or false (F)? Write *T* or *F* in the boxes.**

1 She learned a lot at school. ☐
2 She has learned more since she left school. ☐

b) (14) **Now listen again. In which order did Pat learn to do these things? Write 1–6 in the boxes.**

She learned how to:
drive	☐	cook	☐
swim	☐	speak French	☐
fly an aeroplane	☐	ride a bicycle	☐

c) Are these sentences true (T) or false (F)? Write *T* or *F* in the boxes.

1 Pat learned to swim before she left school. ☐
2 Pat isn't very good at cooking. ☐
3 Pat learned French when she was a child. ☐
4 Pat was good at French. ☐
5 Pat was very good at driving when she started learning. ☐
6 Pat is a good driver. ☐
7 Pat's husband bought her some flying lessons. ☐
8 Pat's daughter didn't want Pat to learn how to fly. ☐
9 Pat thinks that old people can't learn new things. ☐
10 Pat wants to learn how to play the piano. ☐
11 "You can't teach an old dog new tricks" means that older people aren't very good at learning new things. ☐

Work

4 a) Match the beginnings (1–10) and endings (a–j) of these sentences.

1 You have to be good at	a) job security.
2 It's very	b) are important.
3 You have to work	c) a lot of money.
4 You have to be able to	d) stressful.
5 You earn	e) in a team.
6 It's hard work	f) take criticism.
7 There's no	g) dealing with people.
8 The clothes you wear	h) if you can get it.
9 Nobody tells you	i) but enjoyable.
10 It's nice work	j) what to do.

b) Write the letter for the job advertisement (a–c) next to each sentence.

In which job(s) ...
1 do you have to be physically healthy? ....
2 can you decide when you want to work? ....
3 are the clothes you wear important? ....
4 do you have to be good at working in a team? ....
5 do you have to be able to make quick decisions while you are working? ....
6 do you have to be good with people? ....
7 can you expect to develop your career? ....
8 might people say negative things about your work? ....
9 do you have to be able to start tomorrow? ....
10 can you get perks? ....

a) Wanted: Fit person to deliver 'special offer' leaflets for Luigi's Restaurant.
£4 for every 100 leaflets delivered. You decide how many hours you work! Be your own boss! Immediate start.

b) Smartly-dressed secretary needed.
Accounts department of Global Communications.
Must be good at dealing with people.
Ability to think on your feet is essential.
Job security, promotion possible.
Pension scheme. Free gym membership.

c) Bouncers wanted for Club Tropicana
Must be fit, smartly dressed, team player.
Ability to deal with people and work in stressful conditions.
Must be able to take criticism, and deal with people.
Good salary for the right person.
Must be available for immediate start.
Free meals and refreshments.

Verb + -ing

5 a) Gary is applying for a job. Read his letter of application. Circle the correct form.

> **Salesperson wanted.** Recent graduate. Fluent French is essential. Good team worker, persuasive person. Ability to work under pressure in competitive environment. Project management experience. Good salary for the right person.

> Gary Dyer
> 25 Ordinary Avenue
> Normalton
>
> Personnel Manager
> Global Sales Enterprises Inc.
> Gotham City
>
> Dear Sir / Madam
>
> I'm writing **applying / (to apply)** for the job of salesperson, advertised in today's *Daily Globe* newspaper.
>
> I recently graduated from Normal Valley University, where I took a B.A. in French and European Studies.
>
> I am good at **working / to work** [1] in a team, and I also have the ability **work / to work** [2] on my own when necessary. I am very good at **deal / dealing** [3] with people, and I have been told that I am not bad at **persuade / persuading** [4] people, too. I **am working / work** [5] well under pressure, and I like **meet / meeting** [6] new people.
>
> I already have experience of working in telephone sales, as I spent my holidays **sell / selling** [7] advertising space for my uncle's newspaper. I enjoy **to be / being** [8] creative, and am also extremely good at **to make / making** [9] decisions.
>
> **Having / To have** [10] new challenges is important to me, and I am keen to gain more experience in **manage / managing** [11] projects. I am fluent in French, and I love **communicating / communicate** [12] with people from other cultures.
>
> I look forward **hearing / to hearing** [13] from you.
>
> Yours faithfully,
>
> Gary Dyer

b) Gary had an interview with Global Sales Enterprises Inc. Fill in the gaps with the correct verb form.

> make   work (x 2)   deal   persuade (x 3)
> get   swim   sell   apply

INTERVIEWER: Why exactly do you want .... [1] for the job, Mr Dyer?

GARY: Well, I think I'd be quite good at .... [2] your products.

INTERVIEWER: OK. How good are you at .... [3] under pressure?

GARY: Extremely good! After all, I managed .... [4] my degree.

INTERVIEWER: Lots of people do. I need to make sure that you actually want .... [5] under pressure. And I need you .... [6] me that you are the best person for the job.

GARY: Er ... I'm extremely good at ... er .... [7] people, and I'm not bad at .... [8] decisions. I think.

INTERVIEWER: Are you any good at .... [9] with people? Look at me when I'm talking to you!

GARY: I think so. My mother thinks I am.

INTERVIEWER: Well you haven't managed .... [10] me, I'm afraid! Goodbye!!

GARY: I'm not bad at .... [11].

c) 🔊 (15) **Now listen and check.**

Past ability

6 a) Rewrite the underlined parts of the sentences so that the two sentences have the same meaning.

1 I was <u>very good at swimming</u> when I was a child.

   I could .... when I was a child.

2 Climbing the mountain was hard, but in the end we <u>reached the top</u>.

   Climbing the mountain was hard, but in the end we succeeded ....

3 I'm not very good at languages, but I <u>passed</u> my German exam.

   I'm not very good at languages, but I managed

   ....

4 Because the meeting was cancelled, <u>it was possible for me</u> to have a long lunch break.

   The meeting was cancelled, so I .... able

   ....

b) These sentences are incorrect. Change only the underlined words to make them correct.

Example: I <u>managed</u> to read very well when I was four.
   could

1 The train was cancelled, so I took the bus, and I <u>could</u> get to work on time. ....

2 After 15 years doing the same job, Peter <u>could</u> get promoted. ....

3 Colin worked from home, so he <u>managed to</u> choose when he wanted to work. ....

4 It's taken a long time, but I've <u>been able to</u> understanding the Present Perfect! ....

Reading: Brian Labone

Brian Labone played football for Everton, a top English football club, from 1957 to 1971. He joined the club in 1957, when he was seventeen years old, choosing his first love, football, instead of going to university. He played his first full match for the club in 1958, and soon earned a regular place in the side. His main role was as a central defender, and his ability to 'read' the game was excellent. He was tall, and so his natural gift for heading the ball away from danger was valuable to the team. He could also tackle very well, and this also helped Everton on many occasions.

The main weaknesses in his game were his speed, in that he wasn't a very fast runner, and also he preferred to use his right foot rather than his left. Scoring goals was not his strongest point, either, as he only managed to score two during 451 league appearances for the club.

In 1962, Brian Labone was chosen to play for England, and he could have played in the 1966 World Cup final (which England won), but he decided to withdraw from the team in order to concentrate on planning his wedding.

In 1967, he decided that he wanted to retire from football, because he wasn't playing very well. However, after a while, his playing got better, and he stayed at Everton, helping them to win the League Championship in 1969/70. He also played for England again, and went to the World Cup in Mexico, in 1970. Unfortunately, soon after this he was badly injured while playing, and he finally retired in 1971. Brian Labone was not exactly a footballing genius, but his strength and determination made him one of the fans' favourites.

7 a) Read the text quickly, and put these events in the correct order. Write 1–6 in the boxes.

Brian …

celebrated his 17th birthday	☐	joined Everton	☐
played in the World Cup	☐	got married	☐
got badly injured	☐	retired	☐

b) Tick (✓) the correct answer.

1 Brian Labone …
  a) joined Everton when he left university. ☐
  b) didn't go to university. ☐
2 He was …
  a) tall and fast. ☐
  b) tall, but not very fast. ☐
3 He could play better with …
  a) his right foot. ☐
  b) his left foot. ☐
4 a) He scored 451 goals for Everton. ☐
  b) He played 451 matches for Everton. ☐
5 He didn't play in the 1966 World Cup because …
  a) he was getting married. ☐
  b) he went to Mexico instead. ☐
6 a) He wanted to retire in 1966. ☐
  b) He wanted to retire in 1967. ☐
7 a) He retired in 1967. ☐
  b) He retired in 1971. ☐

c) Read the text again, and complete this summary. Use the words in the Word Box.

> could (x 3)   wasn't able   succeeded in
>   managed to   couldn't (x 2)

Brian Labone always loved football, and he

............................(1) play it very well. He ....(2) get

into the Everton team, and so he decided not to go to

university. After a while he became a regular team

member. He ....(3) 'read' the game very well,

and ....(4) also head the ball and tackle. His

weaknesses were that he ....(5) run very fast,

or use his left foot well. He ....(6) to play in

the 1966 World Cup because he was getting married.

However, he played in the World Cup in 1970, when he

............................(7) getting into the team for the

competition in Mexico. He ....(8) play football

again after 1971, because he got injured, and had to

retire from the game.

5 Culture vultures

Cultural events

1 a) Look at the posters. Which one is for: a play ☐ a film ☐ an art gallery ☐ a photography exhibition? ☐

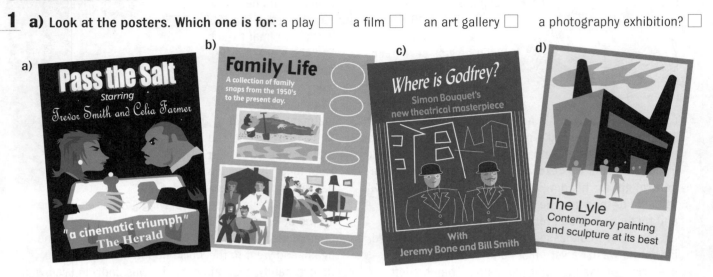

a) **Pass the Salt**
Starring
Trevor Smith and Celia Farmer
"a cinematic triumph"
The Herald

b) **Family Life**
A collection of family snaps from the 1950's to the present day.

c) *Where is Godfrey?*
Simon Bouquet's new theatrical masterpiece
With
Jeremy Bone and Bill Smith

d) **The Lyle**
Contemporary painting and sculpture at its best

b) Now match these reviews to the posters, and fill in the gaps with words from the Word Boxes.

> playwright performances audience play

1 Poster ☐

This is a major new work by .... (1)
Simon Bouquet. The .... (2) from
actors Bill Smith and Jeremy Bone are excellent, and
they successfully interpret Bouquet's economic and
clever use of language, adding to the atmosphere of
oppressive desperation. The .... (3) is inventive,
with subtle humour, and the members of the
.... (4) seemed impressed overall.

> sculpture installation paintings
> exhibition artists

2 Poster ☐

The current .... (1) includes a number of
.... (2) by contemporary .... (3) such as
Italian–Irish genius Salvatore Daly. There is also a giant
marble .... (4) by Terry Lean called "Reclining
Queen", and an .... (5) by Sophie Descanso,
called "My Bathroom", which consists of a recreation of
the artist's bathroom after a night out on the town.

> computers photographs exhibits
> website videos

3 Poster ☐

The collection of family .... (1)
provides an excellent record of family life. For those
who prefer their pictures to move, there are also real
.... (2) of family holidays and parties.
Those with .... (3) can see pictures of
all the .... (4) on the exhibition's
.... (5) .

> director performances box office
> actors film

4 Poster ☐

This is a major new .... (1) from .... (2)
Sidney Oldbrick. Fantastic .... (3)
from the .... (4) capture the potential
nightmare of family life. It's taken a lot of money at the
.... (5), and looks like being a British
success to rival *Billy Biggs, Ballet Boy*.

Subject and object questions

2 **a)** Who gave it to who? Read the text, and join the names up on the diagram. What shape do you get at the end?

○ John

Judy ○   ○ Ann

Bill ○   ○ Fred

It started and finished with John. He thought that Fred might like it, and so he gave it to him for his birthday. But Fred didn't really like it that much, and so Judy got it for Christmas! She thought it was absolutely horrible, and she put it away in a cupboard. One day she showed it to her friend Ann, who thought it was really lovely, and so she took it home. Then when it was Bill's birthday, Ann forgot to buy him a present, and so, in a hurry, she wrapped it up and gave it to him. Bill didn't like it at all, but didn't want to say so. Then, when it was John's birthday, he got it back again, from Bill! He couldn't believe it!

b) Write questions for these answers.

Examples: 1 Who gave it to Fred? John did.

2 ....?   6 ....?

John.   Judy.

3 ....?   7 ....?

Bill did.   He thought he might like it.

4 ....?   8 ....?

Ann.   Because she forgot to
                                                   buy him a present.

5 ....?

Judy did.

c) 〔OO〕 (16) Now listen and check.

d) Look at the questions you wrote for Exercise 2b). Are they subject or object questions? Write *S* (subject) or *O* (object).

e) Look again at your questions for Exercise 2b). Mark the stresses in the questions.

f) 〔OO〕 (16) Now listen and check.

Listening: *Where is Godfrey?*

3 **a)** 〔OO〕 (17) Listen to this extract from the play *Where is Godfrey?*. The two characters we hear are called Vincent and Eric. Are the sentences true (T) or false (F)? Write *T* or *F* in the boxes.

1 Vincent and Eric are talking about an umbrella. ☐
2 Godfrey gave it directly to Eric. ☐

b) 〔OO〕 (17) Listen again, and match the questions (1–6) to the answers (a–f).

1 Who gave it to Jim?   a) Yes, he did.
2 Who did Jim give it to?   b) Because he didn't
3 Why did Sam give it to Arnold?   like the colour.
4 Did Eric give it to Arnold?   c) Yes, he did.
5 Did Eric get it from Arnold?   d) No, he didn't.
6 Did Eric give it to Godfrey?   e) He gave it to Sam.
                                                    f) Godfrey did.

Now fill in the gaps with the names in the Word Box.

╭───╮
│ Eric   Godfrey   Arnold   Jim   Sam │
╰───╯

1 .... didn't give it directly to ....

2 Godfrey gave it to ....

3 Sam got it from ....

4 .... gave it to Arnold, because he didn't like

the colour.

5 .... didn't like the colour either, and so he

gave it to ....

6 .... gave it to Godfrey.

Comparisons

4 **a)** Read this film review. Fill in the gaps with the correct forms of the adjectives in the Word Box.

intelligent	bad	comfortable	fast	insecure	successful	dangerous
creative		unusual	bad	easy	difficult	beautiful

Albert Dinero's latest film, *Bus Driver*, is a lot ....(1) than his early films about ordinary life, as it deals with a man on the edge of society. Dinero plays a clever bus driver, much ....(2) than his colleagues, who becomes dissatisfied with city life. His job is hard, and he begins to find it far ....(3), and quits. The film is quite slow up to this point, but suddenly the action becomes a lot ....(4), as Dinero's character, Bradley Pickle, becomes ....(5), and wants to find his true role in life. Pickle gets involved in some ....(6) situations,

including a plot to kidnap the President of the USA. Things go from ....(7) to ....(8), and he finds himself in prison. When he is released, Pickle's complicated life gets far ....(9) when he finds love, in the shape of poor waitress Imelda Precio (actress Celia Farmer). She is ....(10) than any woman he has ever met, and ....(11) than his previous loves, too (she paints, and writes novels). Imelda writes a ....(12) book (about a bus driver) and they settle down to lead a very ....(13) life in the suburbs.

Movie Star of the Year!

We asked readers to vote on who is the best actor this year. The two biggest films this year have been *Bus Driver* and *Pass the Salt*. Our two finalists were the principal actors from those films, Albert Dinero (*Bus Driver, Hot City Nights*, and many others) and Trevor Smith (*Pass the Salt, Two Paintings*). Here's how you voted, and some movie facts about both actors.

Albert Dinero

Talent rating 10 / 10
Handsome factor 9 / 10
Entertainment value 9 / 10
Intelligence factor 9 / 10
Importance as an actor 9 / 10

Trevor Smith

Talent rating 8 / 10
Handsome factor 2 / 10
Entertainment value 2 / 10
Intelligence factor 8 / 10
Importance as an actor 7 / 10

Facts:

All 17 films have been box-office hits
His recent films have been far from traditional.

Facts:

Pass the Salt was a box-office hit.
Two Paintings was a complete failure.
Both films were boringly traditional.

b) Write sentences to compare how the readers of *Movie Magic* felt about the two actors.
Use *far / a lot* or *slightly / a bit*.

1 Albert .... Trevor. (good at acting)   3 Albert .... Trevor. (important)

2 Albert .... Trevor. (intelligent)   4 Trevor .... Albert. (handsome)

c) 👀 (18) Listen and decide if these sentences are true (T) or false (F). Write *T* or *F* in the boxes.

a) The reviewer talks mostly about *Pass the Salt*, and compares it with *Bus Driver*. ☐
b) Actress Celia Farmer appears in both *Bus Driver* and *Pass the Salt*. ☐
c) *Pass the Salt* has been far more financially successful than *Bus Driver*. ☐
d) *Pass the Salt* is a better film than *Two Paintings*. ☐
e) The character Jane in *Pass the Salt* is a bit more intelligent than her husband, John. ☐
f) The radio reviewer thinks that *Pass the Salt* is far more exciting than *Bus Driver*. ☐
g) The radio reviewer thinks that *Bus Driver* is slightly more difficult to understand than *Pass the Salt*. ☐

Present Perfect Continuous

5 Say what these people do, and what they've been doing. Use the words in the Word Box.

> film director ✓   presenter   picture
> sculpture   concert   artist   poet   sculptor
> write   photographer   poem   make   film ✓
> news   give   take   make ✓   picture
> read   paint   musician

Example: 1 He's a film director. He's been making a film.

2 ....

3 ....

4 ....

5 ....

6 ....

7 ....

Present Perfect Continuous and Present Perfect Simple

6 Rachel and Rebecca used to know each other well, but they haven't seen each other for a long time. Fill in the gaps in their conversation. Use the correct form of the verbs in the Word Box.

> have (x 2)   write (x 2)   complete   make
> see   do (x 2)   set up (a business)

REBECCA: It's Rachel, isn't it?

RACHEL: Rebecca! How are you? I .... (1) you for ages! What .... (2)?

REBECCA: I .... (3) a novel.

RACHEL: Another one! You were writing one the last time I saw you.

REBECCA: Well, it's the same one, I'm afraid.

RACHEL: The same one … Oh, I see. How much .... you .... (4)?

REBECCA: I .... (5) two chapters so far.

RACHEL: How far have you got with chapter 3?

REBECCA: Well, about two pages. Anyway, how about you? What .... you .... (6)?

RACHEL: Well, I .... (7) babies, mainly! I .... (8) three, all boys. Oh, and I .... (9) my own Internet business, too! I .... (10) a million pounds already!

The language of doubt

7 Lucy likes modern art. Derek doesn't. Circle the correct expression in their conversation.

LUCY: Hey, Derek. Look at this. This **looks** / **looks like** interesting. It's called "A Night In".

DEREK: It **looks like** / **looks as if** [1] a bed to me!

LUCY: It **might be** / **looks as if** [2] a comment on modern society.

DEREK: It looks **sort of** / **as if** [3] like something to sleep on.

LUCY: No. You're wrong. **It might be** / **It looks as if** [4] it's telling us something about the way we live. **I suppose it's** / **it looks like** [5] expensive.

DEREK: Well, they're quite cheap at "Beds-U-Like" in the high street …

Listening: *The Colour of Paradise*

8 **a)** 🔊 (19) **Listen to the recording and decide if these sentences are true (T) or false (F). Write *T* or *F* in the boxes.**

1 Mary has been watching a film. ☐
2 Jo has been watching a film. ☐
3 Mary has seen the film. ☐

4 Jo thinks the film is sad. ☐
5 Jo thinks the film is beautiful. ☐

b) 🔊 (19) **Now listen again, and decide if these sentences are true (T) or false (F). Write *T* or *F* in the boxes.**

1 Mohammed's mother has died. ☐
2 Mohammed's father doesn't want him to go to a school for blind children. ☐
3 Mohammed wants to stay at the school. ☐
4 Mohammed doesn't want to live at home. ☐
5 There is a scene where Mohammed is sitting in the school garden. ☐
6 Mohammed tries to put the bird back in its nest, but he can't. ☐
7 The bird is a metaphor for Mohammed. ☐
8 Mohammed goes to work with a carpenter. ☐

c) **Read this summary of the film. Circle the correct forms.**

The Colour of Paradise is an Iranian film about a blind boy called Mohammed. Mohammed's mother (**has died**)/ **was dying**, and his father **has been looking / was looking** (1) after him. When we see Mohammed, he **has been staying / has stayed** (2) at a school for blind children in the city. His father **has wanted / wants** (3) Mohammed to stay at the school, but Mohammed **will like / would like** (4) to go home to the countryside. In one scene, Mohammed **has been sitting / has sat** (5) in the garden of the school. He **has waited / has been waiting** (6) for his father to collect him. He **has heard / has been hearing** (7) a baby bird which **is falling / has fallen** (8) out of its nest. Then he **hears / was hearing** (9) a cat walking towards the bird. So, he **was throwing / throws** (10) stones at the cat to frighten it. Then Mohammed **has found / finds** (11) the baby bird, and manages to put it back in its nest. The bird is a metaphor for Mohammed's situation. He **is wanting / wants** (12) to return to the safety of his home.

d) **Fill in the gaps with *who / where / what*, and match the questions (1–6) to the answers (a–f).**

1 .... wants Mohammed to stay at the school ?

2 .... does his father want him to stay?

3 .... does Mohammed hear the cat?

4 .... has fallen out of the tree?

5 .... does Mohammed want to live?

6 .... goes to work with a carpenter?

a) In the garden.

b) A bird.

c) His father does.

d) At home.

e) Mohammed does.

f) At the school.

e) **Fill in the gaps with *so / such*.**

1 The film is .... beautiful.

2 I don't think I've ever watched .... a sad film.

3 The scene where Mohammed saves the bird is .... moving.

4 The scene where Mohammed saves the bird is .... a moving part of the film.

5 Mohammed looks as if he's .... a gentle boy.

6 Mohammed looks .... lonely when he's sitting in the garden.

6 Skin deep

Clothes

1 a) Look at the pictures of the models. Their names are Fiona and Arsenio. Fill in the gaps, using words from the Word Box.

> flared jeans   tight trousers
> zip   blouse   pockets (x 2)
> trainers   buttons   belt-buckle
> patterned   boots   jacket   T-shirt
> leather jacket

Fiona is wearing a pair of .... ⁽¹⁾. She's also wearing a white .... ⁽²⁾, with .... ⁽³⁾

at the front. The .... ⁽⁴⁾ have .... ⁽⁵⁾ on them. She has a large .... ⁽⁶⁾, and on her feet, she's

wearing black and white leather .... ⁽⁷⁾. Hanging over her shoulder, she has a black .... ⁽⁸⁾.

Arsenio is wearing a tight, white .... ⁽⁹⁾, with a .... ⁽¹⁰⁾ at the front. Hanging over his shoulder, he's

carrying a .... ⁽¹¹⁾ .... ⁽¹²⁾. He's wearing .... ⁽¹³⁾, and on his feet, he's wearing

a pair of black .... ⁽¹⁴⁾.

Pronunciation: word stress

2 a) Underline the stressed syllables in these words.

Example: <u>po</u>lo-neck

short-sleeved	sleeveless	mini
patterned	jacket	jumper
T-shirt	trousers	sweatshirt

b) 🔊 (20) Now listen and check.

c) Underline the main stressed syllables in these words.

Example: polo-neck <u>jum</u>per

high heels	sleeveless jumper
flared trousers	patterned sweatshirt
mini skirt	plain dress
striped top	tight blouse
checked shirt	

d) 🔊 (21) Now listen and check.

e) Circle the correct word, and fill in the gap.

In Exercise 2c), the main stress is in the **first / second**

word, except for ....

Listening: Disco fever!

3 a) 🔊 (22) Listen to Jeremy talking about an old photograph he found, and choose the correct answers.

1 In the photo, Jeremy was …
   a) 14.   b) 40.

2 Who took the photo?
   a) Jeremy   b) Jeremy's sister

3 Jeremy now thinks his clothes …
   a) looked good.   b) didn't look good.

4 His parents…
   a) made him stay at home.   b) took him to the disco.

5 At the time, Jeremy thought his clothes …
   a) looked good.   b) didn't look good.

b) 🔊 (22) Listen again. What did Jeremy wear to the disco? Tick (✓) the words you hear.

platform shoes	boots
green shirt	brown shirt
huge collar	small collar
green stripe	brown stripe
baggy trousers	flared trousers
enormous buckle	small buckle
white short-sleeved jumper	white sleeveless jumper

Superlative adjectives

4 **a)** Write the name of the beauty products (1–4) at the top of each text.

1	2	3	4

bright	fresh	white	smelly

a) ....

Do you smile with confidence? Or do you try to hide your teeth? Use this and be proud of your smile again! Our new formula contains "Thargon X-2" to turn the worst-looking teeth into .... [1], ... [2] teeth you've ever seen. Smokers: does your breath smell? Do people turn away when you breathe? Our new formula will turn .... [3] breath into .... [4].

(Warning: can damage certain metals; use with care)

cheap	quick	good	attractive	young	old

b) ....

.... [1] skin cream product you can buy. It isn't .... [2] face cream, but you won't be wasting your money! Say "goodbye" to wrinkles* and crow's feet* today! This is .... [3] way to make your face look young again – put it on your face once, and your wrinkles disappear. If they come back, simply put it on again! It can turn .... [4] looking face into .... [5], ... [6] one.

*wrinkles are lines on your face. You get more of them as you get older.
*crow's feet are lines which appear at the sides of your eyes.

safe	smooth	long	thick	hairy	old

c) ....

Men ... are you bald? Are you losing your hair? Does this embarrass you? Then you need our new cream. Our scientists say it's .... [1] way to put the hair back on your head. Our special formula can make .... [2] head into the .... [3] one in just two days. Our .... [4] customer is 84 years old, and his head was as smooth as a baby's bottom. After just one application of our new formula, he has .... [5], ... [6] hair he's ever had. You don't need to be bald any more!

cheap	effective	smooth	quick	hairy

d) ....

Men: do you hate shaving? Are you fed up cutting yourself with a razor? Simply apply the cream, and watch your beard disappear. .... [1] beard remover money can buy – so it won't cost you much! Also .... [2] – your beard will disappear in minutes! It can turn .... [3] face into .... [4] in no time at all.

"This is .... [5] product I've ever used. I lost all my hair!" (Mr A. Nidiot, St Mary's Hospital, London)
(From the makers of "Hair Today")

b) Fill in the gaps for each product, using the superlative forms of the adjectives in the Word Boxes.

Second Conditional

5 a) [oo] (23) Listen to Albert Dinero talking, and circle the correct words.

1 Albert is a **film star / a bus driver**.
2 Albert is **rich / poor**.
3 Albert is **famous / not famous**.
4 Albert is **happy / unhappy**.
5 Albert **wants / doesn't want** to change his life.

b) [oo] (23) Listen again, and choose the correct answers.

1 Albert **has / doesn't have** a lot of privacy.
2 Albert **enjoys / doesn't enjoy** going out to restaurants.
3 Albert **likes / doesn't like** people asking for his autograph.
4 Albert **can / can't do** what he wants.
5 Albert **buys / doesn't buy** cheap clothes and ordinary food.
6 Albert **wants / doesn't want** a simple life.
7 Albert **spends / doesn't spend** a lot of time in therapy.
8 Albert **has had / hasn't had** plastic surgery.
9 Albert would prefer to **stay a film star / become a bus driver**.

c) Write sentences to explain how Albert would like to change his life. Use the words in brackets.

Example: not be a film star / be a bus driver (would)
        If I wasn't a film star, I'd be a bus driver.

1 not be a film star / be happy (might)

....

2 happy / not want to change my life (would)

....

3 people not follow me / enjoy going to restaurants (might)

....

4 my life different / do what I want (could)

....

5 buy expensive clothes and food / not enjoy them (would)

....

6 have a simple life / be happier (might)

....

7 happy / not spend a lot of time in therapy (might)

....

8 have plastic surgery / people not recognise me (would)

....

d) Underline the stressed syllables in your sentences for Exercise 5c).

e) [oo] (24) Now listen and check.

Wish + Past Simple

6 These are some of the things Albert Dinero isn't happy about. Write sentences to say how he wishes things were different.

Example: I'm not happy, and I want to be.
        He wishes he were happy.

1 I want to change my life, but I can't.

....

2 People follow me everywhere, and I don't like it!

....

3 I can't enjoy going to restaurants, but I want to!

....

4 I can't do what I want!

....

5 I want a simple life, but I don't have one!

....

6 I spend a lot of time in therapy, and I don't want to!

....

7 I don't want people to recognise me!

....

Body parts

7 Label the body parts in the picture with the words from the Word Box. Use your dictionary if you need to.

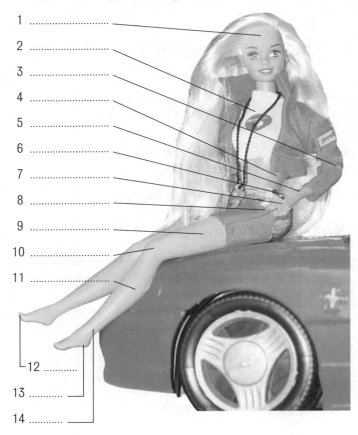

1 ....
2 ....
3 ....
4 ....
5 ....
6 ....
7 ....
8 ....
9 ....
10 ....
11 ....
12 ....
13 ....
14 ....

15 ....
16 ....
17 ....
18 ....
19 ....
20 ....
21 ....

> thumb   neck   elbow   eyelashes   waist
> hips   ankle   heel   shoulder   knee   finger
> thigh   chest   calf   wrist   eyebrows   toe
> forehead   ear   cheek   chin

Infinitives of purpose

8 **a)** Here are some more things people do to their bodies in order to improve or change their appearance. Match these words to the pictures, and circle the correct verb.

Example: 1 (do) / go on yoga   3
            2 go / do weights   ☐
            3 do / have a tattoo   ☐
            4 lie on / have a sunbed   ☐
            5 go on / go jogging   ☐
            6 go on / do a diet   ☐

b) Use the words in the Word Box to say why people do the things in Exercise 8a).

Example: People have plastic surgery to improve their appearance.

> get a tan   concentrate the mind   get fit
> make a personal statement   lose weight
> get bigger muscles

1 (yoga) ....

2 (weights) ....

3 (tattoo) ....

4 (sunbed) ....

5 (jogging) ....

6 (diet) ....

By + verb + *-ing*

9 **a)** Read the passage about Britney once to get a general idea. Tick (✓) the answers to these questions.

1 Has Britney's life changed?   Yes ☐   No ☐
2 Is Britney happier now?   Yes ☐   No ☐

It started about two years ago. I was feeling really unhealthy, I was eating too many sweet things, I was smoking too much, I was drinking too much and I wasn't exercising at all. I was really stressed-out in my job, and one day, it was all too much. I just burst into tears in the office. I couldn't stop crying. I decided that I needed to make some changes. So, how did I do it?

Firstly, I felt a lot better when I gave up smoking. I just stopped, completely. This improved my skin quality almost immediately. I also cut down on alcohol, and because of this I began to lose weight. I was going out every night, so I went out less. Now I only go out one or two evenings a week. As a result, I became more energetic. I also started to go to the gym, and of course I got a lot fitter. Then I went on a diet, and I lost more weight. I cut out all fatty foods, I ate more fruit, I drank more water, and I became a vegetarian. I bought a lot of new clothes, too, and I became more positive as a result. Now my life is much better. I had plastic surgery, too, and I got rid of my wrinkles! Now I'd like bigger lips too …

b) Read the passage again. Britney did things to change her life. Find six ways (not including the example) in which her life improved.

Example: Her skin quality improved.

1 ....
2 ....
3 ....
4 ....
5 ....
6 ....

c) Use the answers to Exercise 9b) and the information in the text to say how Britney made her life better. Use *by* + verb + *-ing*.

Example: She improved her skin quality by giving up smoking.

1 ....
2 ....
3 ....
4 ....
5 ....
6 ....

10 Billy Hill is always ill. Give him some advice about his health problems (1–6). Use a word or expression from each Word Box, and the correct verb forms.

take	put	breathe	tilt

some medicine	an aspirin	some yoghurt on it
into a paper bag		your head back
a plaster on it		some cold water on it

Example: I've got a cough. (try)
Try taking some medicine.

1 I've got hiccups. (how about)

....

2 I've got a nosebleed. (maybe / should)

....

3 I've got sunburn. (should)

....

4 I've got a headache. (why / not / you)

....

5 I've cut my finger. (had better)

....

6 I've burnt my hand. (must)

....

Reading: *Botox*

11 a) Read the article quickly, to get a general idea. Write the headings (a–f) at the beginning of the correct paragraphs (1–6).

a) Goodbye crow's feet.

b) Where does it come from?

c) Why don't more people try to change the way they look?

d) Is it dangerous?

e) How does it work?

f) A new idea.

1 ....

Many people don't want to have cosmetic surgery, because they think it will be painful, and they aren't sure that there will be good results. It is also a very expensive way of improving the way you look. If these factors were not present, a lot more people say that they would consider it.

2 ....

But doctors have developed a way of getting rid of wrinkles and crow's feet quickly, cheaply and with only a little pain.

3 ....

Botox is made from a bacterium called botulin, which is more commonly associated with food that has gone off. You can catch the botulism illness if you eat tinned food (vegetables, like asparagus, and also meat) that hasn't been kept properly. It is also possible for botulin to grow inside a wound, and you can catch the illness in this way, too. Botulism is possibly the most dangerous type of food poisoning.

4 ....

Botulin damages the nerves which join some of your muscles to your brain, but since the 1990s, doctors have used it to help people who have 'facial spasms'. Botulin stops the muscles in their faces moving when they don't want them to.

5 ....

But now, instead of making themselves look younger by having a facelift, many 'supermodels' have begun having treatment with botulin. If you have wrinkles and crow's feet on your face, regular injections of *Botox* (the name of a commercially produced botulin product), it can help to get rid of these lines, and also stop new ones from developing.

6 ....

Doctors who administer *Botox* injections say that the injections don't affect your facial muscles too much, and that you can still show expressions such as surprise and anger. But other doctors have warned that you shouldn't have too many *Botox* injections, because it can lead to damage if you use it over a long period of time. They are also worried that younger people who are treated with *Botox* don't worry so much about the dangers.

b) Are these statements true (T) or false (F)? Write *T* or *F* in the boxes.

1 A lot of people don't want cosmetic surgery because it might hurt, and the results aren't guaranteed. ☐

2 Botulin can make you very ill. ☐

3 You catch botulism every time you eat tinned food. ☐

4 Botulin can be used to treat some medical conditions. ☐

5 *Botox* makes lines appear on your face. ☐

6 Having lots of *Botox* injections is probably very good for your skin. ☐

c) Find words in the text for the following.

1 operations performed by a doctor to improve your appearance (paragraph 1) ....

2 two types of lines on your face (paragraph 2)
.... and ....

3 food that comes in a metal container (paragraph 3)
....

4 an injury which breaks the skin (paragraph 3)
....

5 a condition which means that you can't control the movement of your face (paragraph 4) ....

6 an operation to make your face look younger (paragraph 5) ....

d) Use these ideas to write sentences using *by* + verb + *-ing*.

Example: some people / improve appearance / facelift
          Some people improve their appearance
          by having a facelift.

1 can / get rid of wrinkles / crow's feet / use / *Botox*

....

2 can / become ill / eat tinned food / go off

....

3 doctors / treat some medical conditions / use botulin

....

4 can / damage face / too many / *Botox* injections

....

38

Do you remember? Units 4–6

Revision of verb forms

1 Match the questions (1–5) with the answers (a–e), and fill in the gaps with the correct form of the verbs.

1 How long .... (know) Fred?

2 When .... (get) here?

3 How long .... (have) your dog?

4 How long .... (paint) portraits?

5 .... (finish) writing your novel?

a) No. I .... (do) two chapters so far.

b) I .... (get) it about six months ago.

c) I .... (start) about thirty years ago. I .... (do) it ever since.

d) I .... (arrive) about ten minutes ago.

e) We .... (be) friends for about two years.

2 Complete the sentences using a First or Second Conditional.

Examples: If you pay for the meal, *I'll buy the drinks.* (I / buy / the drinks)

If I had a million pounds *I'd buy a language school.* (I / buy / a language school)

1 If I were you ....
(I / buy her / some flowers)

2 I'll marry you ....
(you promise / love me / forever)

3 I'd walk a million miles ....
(you / ask / me to)

4 If we have a baby ....
(we / not have / enough money / go on nice holidays)

Superlatives

3 Look at this picture of Gemma. Fill in the gaps, using the correct form of the words in the Word Box. Use each word once only.

| weird ✓ | crazy | big | bad | unattractive | expensive |

The ...*weirdest*... thing I've ever done is have my tongue pierced. My mum thinks I'm absolutely mad! In fact she thinks it's the ....(1) mistake I've ever made, especially as I've got an interview for a job tomorrow. She thinks it looks horrible, and that I'll be the ....(2) person there. I suppose I have to admit that this is the ....(3) hairstyle I've ever had. I've had it different colours before, but never cut like this! It's also the ....(4) cut I've ever had. It cost me a fortune! My mum thinks it's the ....(5) thing I could have done. But I like it, and my dad sort of likes it, too!

Crossword

4 Read the clues, and fill in the crossword.

Across ▶

2 You have one on each side of your head.

3 Where the outside of your leg joins your body. Most women have bigger ones than men.

6 It's the bit in the middle of your leg which bends.

8 You have one above each eye.

11 The thickest part of your leg.

12 It's the bit in the middle of your arm which bends.

Down ▼

1 It's at the top of your arm.

4 You have four of these on each hand.

5 You have one of these on each hand.

7 The bit between number 10 and number 1.

9 It's the bit between your hand and your arm which bends.

10 It's at the bottom of your face.

Extend your reading Units 4–6

1 Read the article quickly. Is it about a), b) or c)?

a) finding a new job that suits you
b) using the Internet to find a new job that suits you
c) finding a new job through people that you know

Get career connected ... before someone else lands the job you really want

A year and a half ago, Lisa Imm, 26, wanted a new job in Internet marketing. She needed to network – fast! However, she didn't start attending parties or career fairs and she didn't look in the Sunday paper. Instead, she joined the e-mail list of Web Grrls International, a networking group for women in the technology sector. "I instantly had access to more than 1,000 people," Imm says. "The list is my virtual address book." Imm used the network not only to find available jobs but also to get advice when considering offers. "People wrote back saying, 'I wouldn't work for that company. This is why.' It was like having 100 career counsellors," Imm says. A month later, she landed her job. If you want a new job or career, the Web is the place to start. Here are websites and advice from career coaches that can help you figure out the work you want to do, the best places to do it and the skills you'll need to acquire to get that job.

Most career counsellors agree that finding work that you're passionate about is one of the critical factors behind career success. That's why so many career coaches love diagnostic tools that measure your personality traits, skill levels, professional interests and job potential.

The Web is exploding with tests and assessments you can take without having to go to a career counsellor's office. One of the best is Self-Directed-Search.com. It is based on the theory that people and work environments can be classified into six types: realistic, investigative, artistic, social, enterprising and conventional. The test determines which three types describe you and suggests occupations that could be a good match. To find many tests in one place, visit Yahoo! or another search engine and type "online personality tests" in the search field. You can learn a lot about yourself, and you won't even need a pencil.

2 Read the article again and choose the correct answers for 1–5.

1 Lisa Imm used Web Grrls International to ...
a) get information about new jobs. ☐
b) get advice about particular jobs. ☐
c) do both (a) and (b). ☐

2 Who were the women on Lisa's e-mail list?
a) women who wanted new jobs ☐
b) women who worked in computers ☐
c) women who were career counsellors ☐

3 What does a career coach on the Web offer?
a) training in new skills ☐
b) a list of available jobs ☐
c) advice on finding a job you like ☐

4 Diagnostic tests help you ...
a) decide what kind of job would suit you. ☐
b) feel passion for your future job.v ☐
c) improve your skills. ☐

5 The Self-Directed-Search test ...
a) says there are three types of people. ☐
b) matches people with jobs. ☐
c) matches you with one type of person. ☐

3 Match the words (1–6) to the definitions (a–f).

A	B
1 career counsellor / coach	a) something that can develop
	b) connected to the Internet
2 trait	c) acting in an ordinary, socially accepted way
3 potential	
4 enterprising	d) a quality in a person
5 conventional	e) someone who advises you about suitable work
6 online	f) happy to do new and difficult things

4 Complete the sentences with the correct form of the verbs from the box.

network   land   figure out   acquire   determine

1 I can't .... how this machine works.

2 Our sales this year will .... next year's pay rise.

3 After six months, I managed to .... a place on a management training course.

4 My boss is extremely good at ...., so she knows a huge number of people.

5 It will take three years to .... the necessary qualifications.

5 Read the information about the types of people described in the Self-Directed-Search test. Write the adjectives from the Word Box in the correct place.

> realistic   investigative   artistic
> social   enterprising   conventional

1 .... people:
- usually enjoy creating original work and have a good imagination.
- generally like working with creative ideas and self-expression more than routines and rules.
- are described as disorderly, expressive, idealistic, impractical, open and original.

2 .... people:
- usually have leadership and public speaking abilities, are interested in money and politics, and like to influence people.
- generally like persuading or directing others more than working on scientific or complicated topics.
- are described as agreeable, ambitious, dominant, energetic, outgoing, pleasure-seeking, popular and self-confident.

3 .... people:
- usually have mechanicial and athletic abilities.
- like working outdoors and with tools and machines.
- like working with things more than with people.
- are described as honest, humble, persistent, practical and shy.

4 .... people:
- usually like being around other people, are interested in how people get along, and like to help other people with their problems.
- generally like helping and teaching people more than doing mechanicial or technical activities.
- are described as friendly, generous, helpful, idealistic, tactful and warm.

5 .... people:
- are usually good at maths and science.
- like working alone and solving problems.
- generally like exploring and understanding things or events, rather than persuading others or selling them things.
- are described as curious, independent, precise, rational and reserved.

6 .... people:
- are good at maths.
- like working indoors and organising things.
- like following routines and meeting clear standards.
- are described as careful, efficient, orderly, persistent and practical.

6 Match these occupations (a–f) with types 1–6 in Exercise 5.

a) biologist ☐
b) secretary ☐
c) film director ☐
d) salesperson ☐
e) counsellor ☐
f) electrician ☐

7 Complete the sentences with these adjectives from the text. There are two extra adjectives.

> ambitious   curious   dominant
> persistent   practical   precise
> rational   self-confident

1 Peter likes finding out about all kinds of things. He's very ....

2 Even if something is difficult, I carry on doing it because I want to finish it. I'm ....

3 Sarah's very .... She wants to be the managing director by the time she's thirty.

4 In my job I have to pay attention to the details. I have to be very ....

5 One of my colleagues is very .... She is very sure of her own abilities.

6 Nigel isn't very interested in ideas and theories. He's a really .... person.

8 Put the adjectives from the Word Box into the two groups below.

> agreeable   careful   efficient
> generous   honest   independent
> orderly   original   outgoing
> practical   reserved   tactful

How people behave with others	How people do their work
....	....
....	....
....	....
....	....
....	....
....	....

Extend your grammar Units 4–6

1 Fill in the gaps with words from the Word Box. There are some words you won't need.

ageless	any	but	cute	disagrees	fantasies	fashion	forced	have	position	images
might	no	figure	from	over	that	tells	than	unrealistic	wider	without	would

Barbie's Beauty Problems

Her name is Barbie, she's 39 and she has an extensive list of professions. She is the ....(1) teenage doll that fulfils many young girls' ....(2). With her perfect hair and make-up and her long legs (complete with feet that are frozen in the high-heeled ....(3)), it is amazing that she can handle so many careers ....(4) getting any wrinkles.

........................(5) a professional woman doesn't make it to the top without a few critics, and Barbie is ....(6) exception. What could be considered an innocent toy is under attack ....(7) many women all over the world.

Feminists argue that Barbie's image suggests that girls are only interested in make-up and ....(8). "There is more to life ....(9) dressing up in pretty clothes," says activist Pat Finch. Lauren Goodard, a 26-year-old law student and active feminist, says, "I'm not going to blame all of my problems on Barbie, but that doll definitely reinforces negative ....(10) about women. It makes our little girls think that they ....(11) to be tall and skinny to get a good job or a ....(12) boyfriend."

The fact is that Barbie is pretty, she's successful, she gets 120 new outfits made for her a year and she has ....(13) a billion pairs of shoes. She is also ....(14). If Barbie were a real woman, she ....(15) be 1.68m tall and her measurements would be 99–53–84cm.

As the first step towards correcting her exaggerated ....(16), this year Barbie will be getting a new look. She will have a ....(17) waist, smaller bust, and flat feet. She will also have a new nose, closed mouth and softer, straighter hair. Feminists ....(18) think that their protest ....(19) Mattel to change Barbie's figure, but Mattel ....(20). "I think Barbie is an extremely positive doll," says Mattel Consumer Affairs spokesperson, Bobby Reid. "We changed Barbie's body because little girls wanted a change, not because we feel Barbie is bad for girls' self-image … she is the Queen of fashion."

2 Complete the second sentence so that it means the same as the first sentence.

Example: It's not necessary to know how to type to use a computer.

You don't _have to know how_ to use a computer.

1 She finally managed to get the job she wanted.

She was finally .... the job she wanted.

2 It is difficult to find the perfect dress for you.

Finding .... difficult.

3 I have spent all morning talking on the phone.

I have .... all morning.

4 Other dolls aren't quite as famous as Barbie.

Barbie is far .... other dolls.

5 If you eat properly, you can lose weight.

You can lose weight by .... properly.

6 The film is so scary that some people walk out before it's finished.

It's such .... some people walk out before it's finished.

7 I can't become an actress because I am too shy.

If I weren't .... become an actress.

8 It's a pity that he can't be here.

I wish .... here.

Extend your writing Units 4–6

Writing a formal letter

1 Do you remember the format of a formal letter?
Complete the outline with information from the box.

> Dear Sir or Madam   Best wishes
> Yours faithfully   Yours sincerely   Dear Mr / Ms
> Date   Your name   Your address
> Their name   Their address   Your signature

....

....

....

....

....

Body of the letter

....

....

....

2 Look at the advertisement below which was in *The Guardian* newspaper on 26 June.

> We are a busy film company looking for a Production Assistant to work in our travel and history department. We make films for both TV and commercial companies and are looking for a flexible and organised assistant to the film directors. Experience in the film world is not necessary but you should have experience of working to deadlines in a team. You should be able to think quickly in stressful situations and be available to work long hours. An interest/qualifications in the areas of history and/or travel would be useful.
>
> All letters of application and CVs to:
> Laura Spencer, Dude Ranch Studios,
> 48 Waterford Lane, London, SW10, England.

You would like to apply for the job. Write a covering letter to accompany your CV. Use the words given below to make complete sentences and then organise them into paragraphs. Make sure that you use the correct format and language for a formal letter of application.

Responsible / organise / work schedule / department.

Yours sincerely,

Look / forward / hear / you.

As / see / CV, / history degree / and / currently / work / travel desk / national newspaper.

In addition, / appreciate / chance / use / background / history.

Thank / considering / application.

Work / team / journalists, / photographers / artists.

Manage / list / current jobs / make sure / completed / on time.

Dear Ms Spencer,

Often / work late / night / and / weekends.

Feel / therefore, / have / qualifications and experience / necessary / job.

I / write / response / advertisement / production assistant / *The Guardian* newspaper / 26 June.

7 Can we talk?

Communication

1 **a)** Match the communication verbs (1–11) to the nouns (a–i). Most verbs have more than one match.

Example: send goes with c), e), g) and i).

Verbs	Nouns
send .c), e), g), i)............	a) a phone call
1 make	b) a mobile phone
2 get	c) a letter
3 attach	d) a message
4 write	(on an answering machine)
5 leave	e) an e-mail
6 reply to	f) a computer
7 open	g) a text message
8 turn on	h) a telephone
9 delete	i) a document
10 read	
11 listen to	

b) Fill in the gaps with verbs from Exercise 1a). Use the correct form of the verb.

1 I .... a text message from my girlfriend,

saying "I love you". I .... it immediately, but I

think I .... it to the wrong number!

2 I .... an important e-mail from my boss. I

hadn't read it yet, and I accidentally .... it.

3 The first thing I do when I get home is .... the

messages on my answering machine, and ....

some phone calls. Then, I .... the computer,

and .... my e-mails. Then I say "hello" to my wife.

4 I'm trying to .... an e-mail to my boss, but I

don't know how to .... a document to it. Can

you help me?

5 I love using e-mail. .... letters takes a lot of

time, so e-mails are much more convenient.

6 I .... a message on Tim's answering machine

to let him know where to meet us.

7 I .... so many e-mails at work that I don't have

time to read them all! So, I just .... the ones

that look important, and .... the others.

c) Fill in the gaps with words from the Word Box.

> read   keep in touch   send   make
> access   attach   write

AS SEEN ON TV!

Do you hate wasting time? Do you like to impress your boss? With the new *Pocket Pal* you can do your work while travelling to the office, and then ask your boss to give you some more to do! You're sure to get a higher salary, and promotion too!

With the *Pocket Pal* you can

- ....(1) the Internet.

- ....(2) documents to your e-mails.

- read, write and ....(3) letters, faxes and other documents.

- ....(4) speeches and prepare presentations.

- ....(5), write and send e-mails.

- ....(6) phone calls. (Yes! It's also a mobile phone!)

- send text messages.

- ....(7) with your kids as they go to school.

- iron your shirt. (Hey! Not really! But there isn't much that the *Pocket Pal* can't do!)

- Have you got two minutes to relax? You can also listen to music on the *Pocket Pal*. Simply record your CDs onto your home PC, download them onto the *Pocket Pal*, plug in the special adapter, change the hard disk, convert the music files to PP3 format, and ... enjoy!

d) Tick (✓) five things you could do with a Pocket Pal.

a) write a message and send it to yourself at work, to remind yourself to do something ☐
b) communicate with your boss while you are sitting on a train ☐
c) make your shirt look nicer ☐
d) call a theatre to book tickets ☐
e) make a speech ☐
f) find a web page ☐
g) take your children to school ☐
h) receive a phone call from your wife / husband ☐
i) turn on the television ☐

Past Perfect Simple or Past Simple?

2 **a)** Fill in the gaps in this story using words in the Word Box.

lose	miss	pick up	leave	miss
get	manage	have to	(never) fly
find	stay	open	leave	give

The holiday was a complete disaster! On the way to the airport, we ....(1) our train, so when we got there, the plane ....(2)! We ....(3) to catch a later flight, but we ....(4) wait a long time. I was really nervous, because I ....(5) before! When we eventually got to our hotel, we found that they ....(6) our room to another couple. Anyway, they ....(7) us a room at another hotel, and we ....(8) there. When I ....(9) my suitcase, though, I realised that it wasn't mine. I ....(10) the wrong suitcase at the airport! So, I had to use my credit card, and buy some clothes. The rest of the holiday was quite nice, but the journey back was horrible! We ....(11) our flight again, because when we got to the airport, Sophie couldn't find her passport! She ....(12) it at the hotel. So, we had to go back to the hotel, find the passport, and get another flight. If all of that wasn't enough, when we eventually ....(13) home, I realised I ....(14) my key. I remember having it with me on the plane, so perhaps I lost it on the journey. I need another holiday to get over that one!

b) 🔊 (25) **Now listen and check.**

c) Put these events from the story in Exercise 2a) in the correct order. Number them 1–11.

The plane left. ☐
They arrived home. ☐
They got to the airport. ☐
They went to another hotel. ☐
They arrived at their hotel. ☐
He lost his key. ☐
He realised he had the wrong suitcase. ☐
The hotel gave their room to another couple. ☐
They got to the airport. ☐
Sophie left her passport at the hotel. ☐
They missed their train. ☐

d) Circle the correct form in these sentences.

My house was burgled last year. When I **got / had got**[(1)] home from work, I **realised / had realised**[(2)] that someone **broke / had broken**[(3)] in, because the front door **was / had been**[(4)] open. They **stole / had stolen**[(5)] my TV and video, and they **threw / had thrown**[(6)] all my clothes on the floor. I **thought / had thought**[(7)] that they **didn't take / hadn't taken**[(8)] anything else. However, two months later, when I **wanted / had wanted**[(9)] to go on a business trip, I **realised / had realised**[(10)] that they **took / had taken**[(11)] my passport, too!

So and *because*

3 **a)** Match the events from the two columns.

1 Someone / steal / everything
2 My car / break down / on the motorway
3 I / not study / the grammar
4 I / not be / hungry
5 They / have an argument
6 The room / be empty
7 I / never fly / before
8 He / not have / any money

a) He / buy / her / some flowers
b) I / do / it before
c) I / already / have lunch
d) I / forget / to put petrol in it
e) Everyone / go
f) He / phone / the police
g) He / forget / his wallet
h) I / feel / a bit nervous

b) Now write sentences with *so* or *because* for the ideas in Exercise 3a). Use the events on the left first.

Example: 1 Someone had stolen everything, so he phoned the police.

2 ....

3 ....

4 ....

5 ....

6 ....

7 ....

8 ....

Reported speech

4 a) Change these sentences from Reported Speech to Direct Speech.

Example: She said she hadn't told him yet.
"I haven't told him yet."

1 He told me he would phone me.

....

2 Amanda said she was coming to the party.

....

3 He said that his computer had crashed.

....

4 Stefania told Kurt she loved him.

....

5 She said it was easy to learn English.

....

6 He told her that he loved her, and that he would never leave her.

....

7 She said that she would phone him the next day.

....

8 The mechanic told her that it wasn't a big problem, and that it would be easy to fix.

....

b) 〔oo〕 (26) Now listen and check.

Listening: Rodney and the party

5 a) 〔oo〕 (27) Listen to Rodney talking about a party, and say if these sentences are true (T) or false (F). Write *T* or *F* in the boxes.

1 There was a misunderstanding. ☐
2 The couple went to a party. ☐
3 The man went to the party. ☐
4 The woman stayed at home. ☐
5 There was a man called Rodney at the party. ☐
6 The woman who gave the party knows the man telling the story very well. ☐

b) From the story, who said these sentences?

1 The party has been cancelled, Rodney. ....

2 Maria, has the party been cancelled? ....

3 No, Clarissa, the party is still on. ....

4 No, this isn't my husband. ....

5 Why didn't you come to the party? ....

6 I thought the party had been cancelled. ....

c) Change the sentences from Exercise 5b) from Direct Speech to Reported Speech. Use names to make it clear who said what.

Example: 1 John told Rodney that the party had been cancelled.

2 ....

3 ....

4 ....

5 ....

6 ....

Reported questions

6 a) Only two of these sentences (1–7) are correct. Tick (✓) them, and correct the other sentences.

1 She asked them whether could he fix her car.
2 The journalist asked him if did he think the team would win.
3 He asked him if he lived in the town centre.
4 She asked me where I worked.
5 She asked me where did I live.
6 Her asked her where had she met her boyfriend.
7 She asked them where did they come from.

a) ....

b) ....

c) ....

d) ....

e) ....

b) Now write the questions which were reported in Exercise 6a).

Example:

1 *Can you fix my car?* ....

2 ....

3 ....

4 ....

5 ....

6 ....

7 ....

Telephoning: phrasal verbs

7 **a)** Fill in the gaps in the conversations with the correct form of the verbs in the Word Box.

> ring up   get back   put through
> take down   hang up   call back (x 2)
> look up   get through   cut off

1 A: Hello, Digby Communications. How can I help you?

B: Hello, could you .... me .... (1) to Mrs Dimchester?

A: I'm afraid she's out of the office at the moment. Can you .... (2) later?

B: Certainly.

2 A: Hello, Kovach and Noble Advertising. Can I help you?

B: Hello there. I'm trying to .... (3) to Dexter Flynn. I was talking to him a moment ago, and I got .... (4). Is he there?

A: I'm afraid Mr Flynn has just gone into a meeting. Let me .... (5) your name and number, and I'll get him to .... you .... (6) later.

B: Sorry, I can't hear you very well. Could you say that again?

A: If you give me your name and number, he'll .... (7) to you later.

B: OK, thanks. It's Albert Collingwood.

3 A: Hello, I'm sorry to .... you .... (8) so late in the evening, but is Katerina there?

B: I'm sorry, there's nobody here called Katerina. You must have the wrong number.

A: I'm very sorry, I .... (9) the number in the book ... Oh, he's .... (10). How rude!

b) 📼 (28) **Now listen and check.**

Informal telephone language

8 **a)** Beth is phoning her friend Vanessa. Put the sentences (1–9) in the right order to make a conversation.

1 Hi there, Vanessa.
2 Where are you going?
3 Really well, thanks. I passed my exam!
4 Fantastic! Well done!
5 To that new restaurant on the high street. Do you fancy coming?
6 Thanks. I'm going out tonight with some friends to celebrate.
7 About seven-thirty.
8 Hi Beth, how are you?
9 I'd love to. What time?

BETH: Hi there, Vanessa.

VANESSA: ....

BETH: ....

VANESSA: ....

BETH: ....

VANESSA: ....

BETH: ....

VANESSA: ....

BETH: ....

b) 📼 (29) **Now listen and check.**

c) Mark the stressed syllables on the conversation in Exercise 8a).

d) 📼 (29) **Now listen again and check.**

Listening: Mobile madness

9 **a)** 🔘🔘 (30) Maria has had an argument with her boyfriend Danny.
Listen as she tells her friend Kate about it, and answer the questions. Tick (✓) the correct answers.

1 Maria had an argument with Danny, and …
   a) everything is now fine. ☐
   b) they haven't seen or spoken to each other since. ☐
   c) they have seen each other, but had another argument. ☐

2 Maria and Danny argued because …
   a) Danny doesn't contact her often enough. ☐
   b) Danny uses his mobile phone too much. ☐
   c) Danny is always borrowing Maria's mobile phone. ☐

b) 🔘🔘 (30) Now listen again, and tick (✓) the correct answers.

1 Danny called from the train to say that …
   a) he was coming to see Maria. ☐
   b) he couldn't come to see Maria. ☐
   c) he had lost his mobile phone. ☐

2 The next place that Danny phoned from was …
   a) a florist's. ☐
   b) a pub. ☐
   c) the street. ☐

3 Maria was annoyed because …
   a) she couldn't hear Danny properly. ☐
   b) she wanted to watch a film with Danny. ☐
   c) she was trying to watch a film, and Danny's phone calls interrupted her. ☐

4 When Danny phoned from the bus, Maria told him …
   a) to keep phoning her to let her know when he would arrive. ☐
   b) not to phone her again. ☐
   c) to buy a better telephone. ☐

5 Danny phoned from the florist's to ask …
   a) what sort of flowers Maria liked. ☐
   b) what sort of flowers Maria's mother liked. ☐
   c) whether Maria wanted some flowers. ☐

6 Danny phoned from outside Maria's front door because …
   a) he wanted to play a trick on her. ☐
   b) he was angry with her. ☐
   c) he couldn't find the doorbell. ☐

So and *because*

c) Match the beginnings (1–7) and endings (a–g) of these sentences. Use *so* / *because* to fill in the gaps.

Beginning	Ending
1 Maria and Danny haven't seen each other for a while	a) .... he phoned from the florist's.
2 Danny kept phoning Maria on his mobile	b) .... she wanted to invite her to a wedding.
3 Danny wanted to know what sort of flowers Maria's mother liked	c) .... they had an argument.
4 Danny wanted to play a trick on Maria	d) .... she got angry.
5 Maria got really angry	e) .... he phoned her from outside her front door.
6 Lisa phoned Maria	f) .... she wanted to phone Danny.
7 Maria asked to borrow Kate's mobile	g) .... Danny phoned her from the bathroom.

Past Perfect Simple and Past Simple

d) Fill in the gaps with the correct form of the verbs in brackets. You also need to decide where each verb goes.

Example: Danny ...*phoned*... Maria and told her he ...*had bought*.. a new mobile phone. (buy / phone)

1 Danny .... again to tell Maria that he .... a friend. (phone / meet)

2 Danny .... that it was Maria's mother's birthday, so he .... from the florist's. (phone / remember)

3 When Danny .... from the florist's, the film .... (phone / finish)

4 Lisa .... because she .... to invite Maria to a wedding. (want / phone)

5 I .... the phone so many times that I .... the funny side. (not see / answer)

8 Life, death and the universe

Predicting the future

Degrees of certainty

1 **a)** Put the expressions in order from 1–6.

a) It definitely won't happen. [1]
b) It'll probably happen. ☐
c) It might happen. ☐
d) It probably won't happen. ☐
e) It'll definitely happen ☐
f) It might not happen. ☐

Will and going to

c) Match the ideas (1–5) to the reasons / evidence (a–e). Then decide if you need to use *will* or *going to*, and write a sentence.

Example: my wife / buy me some socks / for my birthday
My wife will buy me some socks for my birthday.
She always does.

1 Bujunga language / disappear.

....

2 Anna / be late.

....

3 They / meet again / before the end.

....

4 Trevor / get married.

....

5 There / be / an election.

....

Going to + verb

b) Fill the gaps with *to be* + *going to* + a verb from the Word Box.

fall down	die	rain ✓
teach	have	crash	hit

Example: It's going to rain. There are dark clouds overhead.

1 We .... all .... ! The asteroid is

heading straight for Earth!

2 She .... him. She's really annoyed.

3 That car .... !

It's going straight towards the wall.

4 His trousers .... I've seen this film before.

5 She .... a baby. Her tummy is very big.

6 David .... us how to talk about the future.

I saw his timetable on his desk.

a) She phoned, and told me her train has been delayed.

b) I've seen films like this before.

c) The President has resigned.

d) He and Jane have got engaged.

e) The only person who speaks it is a 98-year-old woman.

Listening: *In the House*

2 a) 🔊 (31) **Listen to John and Jane talking about the television programme *In the House*. Tick (✓) the correct answers.**

1 How interested is John in the programme?
a) very ☐   b) a little ☐   c) not at all ☐
2 How interested is Jane in the programme?
a) very ☐   b) a little ☐   c) not at all ☐

b) 🔊 (31) **Read these questions, and listen again. Tick (✓) the correct answers.**

1 How many people are in the house?
a) 9 ☐   b) 10 ☐   c) 1 ☐
2 How many weeks do they stay in the house?
a) 10 ☐   b) 9 ☐   c) 1 ☐
3 Do all of them stay until the end?
Yes ☐   No ☐
4 Which of these sentences is correct?
a) The viewers decide which two people
   should leave the house each week.   ☐
b) The people in the house decide which
   person should leave each week.   ☐
c) The people in the house choose two people
   to leave, and the public votes for one of them.   ☐
5 You can watch "In the House" on the Internet.
Yes ☐   No ☐

Will and *going to*

c) John and Jane are watching *In the House* on TV. Use *will* / *'ll* or *be going to* (or the negative forms) to complete their conversation.

JOHN: Oh, no! Patty has to leave the house! She's been

voted out! Look, I think she ....(1) start crying.

JANE: No, she ....(2) cry, she's just got something in

her eye.

JOHN: I read in the newspaper that she ....(3)

record a song when she comes out.

JANE: Oh, dear. That's a bad idea. It ....(4)

probably be awful.

JOHN: What about Matty? What do you think ....(5)

happen to him?

JANE: I'm not sure. But he definitely ....(6) stay in

the house until the end. In fact, I think the viewers

...................(7) probably vote him out next weekend.

JOHN: Maybe, maybe not. We ....(8) see when

the time comes.

JANE: I think Hattie might stay a bit longer. I think she

...........................(9) still be there next week.

JOHN: Yes, you're right. But she's starting to annoy the

other contestants. Hey look! She ....(10)

kiss Matty! No! I was wrong. She ....(11)

kiss Warren.

JANE: Oh! She's so annoying! Anyway. You told me you

...........................(12) watch this programme!

JOHN: No, I said I *might* not watch it.

d) 🔊 (32) **Now listen and check.**

Otherwise and in case

3 Use these ideas to write sentences using *otherwise* / *in case*.

Example: Bring your umbrella: You'll get wet. /
It might rain.
Bring your umbrella, otherwise you'll get wet.
Bring your umbrella in case it rains.

1 Don't forget to video the evening news: You won't see
your brother talking to that pop star. / Maybe your
brother will be on it.

a) ....

b) ....

2 I'll take some cash with me: They might not take
credit cards. / I won't be able to pay!

a) ....

b) ....

3 We'd better not walk: We won't get there on time. /
Maybe it's a long way.

a) ....

b) ....

4 I'll bring the key: You might want to look around the
new house. / You won't be able to look around.

a) ....

b) ....

5 I'm going to study the Present Perfect: It might come
up in the test. / I won't know it for the test.

a) ....

b) ....

Third Conditional

had important job
▼
felt stressed all the time
▼
argued with boss
▼
lost job
▼
argued with my wife
▼
wife left me
▼
lost interest in life
▼
ended up here …

meet Ida
▼
feel happy
▼
become interested in life again
▼
find a job
▼
earn some money
▼
be able to invest the money
▼
become rich
▼
buy a big house.

Where did it all go wrong?

4 a) What is Ian thinking? Use the Third Conditional to write sentences.

Example: *If I hadn't had an important job, I wouldn't have felt stressed all the time.*

1 ....
2 ....
3 ....
4 ....
5 ....
6 ....
7 ....

b) Now write sentences to explain the next part of Ian's life.

1 If I ....
2 ....
3 ....
4 ....
5 ....
6 ....
7 ....
8 ....

5 Look at these sentences. Decide which sentences show blame, relief or regret.

1 If you hadn't told me to invest in your brother's company, I wouldn't have lost all my money. ...*blame*...

2 If I hadn't been able to invest the money, I wouldn't have become rich. ....

3 If I hadn't felt stressed all the time, I wouldn't have argued with my boss. ....

4 If you'd told me your mother was coming for Christmas, I would have bought her a present. ....

5 If I hadn't felt happy, I wouldn't have become interested in life again. ....

6 If I hadn't argued with my boss, I wouldn't have lost my job. ....

Pronunciation: *have* / sentence stress

6 **a)** How is *have* pronounced in these sentences?
Mark them **S** (strong) if it's pronounced as /æ/
Mark them **W** (weak) if it's pronounced as /ə/

1 If I'd <u>seen</u> him, I would have <u>told</u> him. [W]
2 I haven't seen John yet. Have you? [ ]
3 What time did you have dinner last night? [ ]
4 I'm sure I would have seen her if she'd been there. [ ]
5 Have you done your homework yet? [ ]
6 You wouldn't have lost your job if you
hadn't shouted at the boss. [ ]

b) Underline the stressed syllables in the
sentences in Exercise 6a).

c) 📼 (33) Now listen and check.

7 **a)** Read the text and decide if the sentences 1–4
are true (T) or false (F). Write *T* or *F* in the boxes.

Enrico, 28 years old
I come from Pontevedra, in the north-west of
Spain. I came to England five years ago, just for
three months, to study English at a school in
London. After two weeks, I met Sachiko, and we
fell in love. I never went back to Spain, except for
our wedding. Now we both live and work in
London, where we run our restaurant, El Sushi. I
knew nothing about the restaurant business
before I met Sachiko. She taught me everything.
Now we have a house in London, a holiday home in
Pontevedra and another house in Osaka.

1 Enrico met Sachiko when he came to London. [ ]
2 They got married in England. [ ]
3 Enrico ran a restaurant before he met Sachiko. [ ]
4 Sachiko knew a lot about how to run a restaurant. [ ]

b) All of these sentences are grammatically correct.
However, two of them are meaningless. Put *R*
(right) or *W* (wrong).

1 If he hadn't come to London, he wouldn't have
met Sachiko. [ ]
2 If he hadn't studied English, he would have gone
back to Spain. [ ]
3 If he hadn't met Sachiko, he might not have learned
how to run a restaurant. [ ]
4 If he hadn't been Spanish, he wouldn't have
bought a house in Osaka. [ ]

Points of view

8 **a)** Choose the appropriate ending for each
conversation from the sentences / phrases in the
Word Box.

[You must be joking   Be a sport   I can't argue with that]

1 A: Please, we need one more player to complete the
team.
B: Well, I'm not sure.

A: ....

[I see your point   I see what you mean   If you ask me]

2 A: You've got to tell him.
B: But he'll be really shocked!

A: .... , you haven't got any choice.

[You must be joking   I see your point   Just have a go]

3 A: I really don't want to, OK?
B: Don't be such a wimp. It won't bite.

A: .... Look at those teeth.
B: Look. I'll do it. Aaaaaaargh!

[That's true   I suppose so   I don't think so]

4 A: It's quite a small car.
B: It's big enough for us and the children. And your
mother.

A: .... We've got six children, remember?
B: I see your point.

b) 📼 (34) Now listen and check.

c) Read Exercise 8a) again. In which conversation
is Speaker A doing these things? Write the number
of each conversation.

a) Disagreeing [ ]
b) Giving an opinion [ ]
c) Refusing to be persuaded [ ]
d) Persuading [ ]

Reading: Barry Oakley – "Mr Karaoke"

9 a) Read the article, and match the questions (1–6) to Barry's answers (a–f).

1 Have you any advice for people who want to get up and sing?
2 How long have you been doing it?
3 Have you always been a good singer?

4 Have you tried becoming a professional singer?
5 How did you start doing it?
6 What makes your nights better than others?

REAL LIVES

Continuing our series on real lives, we met Barry Oakley, who organises karaoke singing nights in pubs and clubs all over the UK.

a) ....
I started organising karaoke nights three years ago, and I think it's the best job I've ever had.

b) ....
By accident, really. My girlfriend and I went out one evening to a pub, with some friends. The pub was having a karaoke night, and lots of people were getting up to sing. I'd never been to one before. Some of my friends did it, and Sharon, my girlfriend, had a go too. When she sat down after singing, she tried to persuade me to have a go. But I just refused. The thought of getting up to sing on a stage absolutely terrified me. But then my friends joined in, trying to persuade me. Then Jim, one of my friends, told the organisers to announce my name. When I heard my name, I felt I had to. I would have felt stupid if I hadn't. If Jim hadn't done that, I wouldn't have got up to sing. No way!

c) ....
Well, I didn't know I was a good singer until that night. I started singing, and the crowd just went wild! They loved me! I wanted to stay on that stage forever!

d) ....
I released one CD, called *The Writing's On The Wall*, but it didn't sell very well. I'm glad I did, because I realised that my voice is good, but not good enough to be a serious singer. That's when I had the idea of organising my own karaoke nights.

e) ....
Three things. The equipment, the entertainment, and making people feel comfortable about singing. I bought the best equipment with the money I made from my CD. If I hadn't invested that money in equipment, I don't think I'd have been so successful. Entertaining people is important, too. I always start off by singing a couple of songs myself. You have to do this, or people won't want to get up and sing. You also have to make people feel good about singing. If you make them feel silly or stupid, either they won't do it, or they won't come back the next time.

f) ....
Yeah! Just do it. If you think about it for too long, you'll get nervous. Just get up there and enjoy yourself!

b) Join these ideas together to make Third Conditional sentences.

Example: I went to the karaoke night.
I found a job I really enjoy.
If I hadn't gone to the karaoke night,
I wouldn't have found a job I really enjoy.

1 Jim told the organisers to announce my name. I got up to sing.

....

2 I got up to sing when they announced my name. I didn't feel stupid.

....

3 I got up to sing. I realised I was a good singer.

....

4 I released a CD. I had enough money to buy good equipment.

....

5 I invested my money in good equipment. My karaoke nights became successful.

....

c) Jim is trying to persuade Barry to get up and sing. Who said what? Write *J* (Jim) or *B* (Barry) for each sentence.

a) Look, I really don't want to. [B] [ ]

b) You can't be serious! My voice is awful! [ ] [ ]

c) Oh come on, I've heard you sing in the shower. You've got a great voice! [ ] [ ]

d) No, it isn't! Don't be such a wimp! You only live once … [ ] [ ]

e) If I could sing, I'd be on stage now. Go on, be a sport. [ ] [1]

Now put the sentences in order to make a conversation. Write 1–5 in the boxes.

⑨ It's a family affair

Celebrations

1 In the Word Square, find the words which complete the sentences (1–11). Words can go down, across or diagonally, ↓ → ↘ ↗.

R	F	H	M	C	A	N	D	L	E	S
E	O	E	A	H	E	U	R	I	C	J
C	A	F	R	G	R	M	B	S	H	K
E	R	P	Q	U	I	N	I	U	O	T
P	C	D	U	E	S	F	R	B	S	E
T	P	R	E	S	E	N	T	O	R	A
I	S	A	E	T	L	G	H	L	C	I
O	E	K	T	B	R	I	D	E	I	N
N	A	N	S	R	A	S	A	C	B	L
C	E	R	E	M	O	N	Y	D	W	I

1 A wedding _ _ _ _ _ _ _ _ is usually held in a church or a registry office.

2 A _ _ _ _ _ _ is invited to a celebration or party.

3 A _ _ _ _ gives a party, and invites people.

4 You have a _ _ _ _ _ _ _ _ each year on the day that you were born.

5 If you go to a party, you might give your (3) a _ _ _ _ _ _ _.

6 Another word for (5) _ _ _ _.

7 People eat _ _ _ _ for birthdays, weddings and Christmas.

8 You find _ _ _ _ _ _ _ on a (7). You have to blow them out and make a wish.

9 A large tent. Some people hold their (10) in a _ _ _ _ _ _ _.

10 The party after a wedding is known as the _ _ _ _ _ _ _ _.

11 A woman who is getting married is a _ _ _ _ _.

2 a) Read the poem about a family celebration, and fill in the gaps with words from the Word Box.

> strangers   musicians   marquee   argument
> invitations   champagne   caviar   great-aunty
> gifts   families   friends   replies   steak   chefs
> drink   host   guests   great-uncle   beer
> comedian   decorations   loaf of bread

The Family Party

The party was father's idea
He was missing his long-lost relations
His cousins, their mothers, their sisters and brothers
Who all lived in various nations.

My mother sent out .... (1)
The .... (2) were quite slow coming back
And one from Romania, postmarked "Transylvania"
Had a smear of blood on the back.

They hired a .... (3) for the garden
And a couple of .... (4) for the food
A group of .... (5), a pair of magicians
And a .... (6) who wasn't too rude.

And then on the day of the party
There were .... (7) from all over the planet
And one or two .... (8), who presented no danger
And a small chimpanzee, called Janet.

The .... (9) looked lovely
And people bought .... (10) for the .... (11)
There was .... (12) and cake, some chicken
and .... (13)
And .... (14), olives and toast.

But .... (15) bring complications
And an .... (16) started quite soon
Between .... (17) Bert, who got wine on his shirt
And my cousin's .... (18), called June.

Then everything seemed to go wrong
Food and .... (19) flew through the air
A big .... (20) hit my dad on the head
Followed quite soon by a chair.

When the .... (21) left, there was silence
My father sat, drinking a .... (22)
With his hands on his head, then he suddenly said
"Shall we do it again, every year?"

b) 👀 (35) Now listen and check.

Regrets: I've had a few

1

Oh no... my wife!

2

3 GIVING UP SMOKING DIARY — DAYS SINCE I GAVE UP SMOKING

4

5

6

read / invitation   have / car serviced
start / smoking   come here ✓
listen / my mother   become / teacher

3 **a)** Write sentences to explain the regrets these people have. Use *should* / *shouldn't* + past participle.

Example: 1 _We shouldn't have come here._

2 ....

3 ....

4 ....

5 ....

6 ....

b) Which three sentences from Exercise 3a) can be rewritten using *should never*? Write them here.

1 ....

2 ....

3 ....

c) Now look again at pictures 1–6. Use the ideas in the box to write sentences using *I wish* / *If only*.

ask if it was fancy dress   buy a different car
go somewhere else ✓   finish my marking earlier
give up when I was younger   marry Bud instead

Example: 1 _If only we'd gone somewhere else._

2 I wish ....

3 If only ....

4 I wish ....

5 If only ....

6 I wish ....

Revision: Conditional sentences

d) Look back at the pictures in Exercise 3a). Match the ideas (1–6) with the ideas (a–f).

1 not go to that bar ⟍   a) not have so much work
2 listen / my mother ⟍ ⟋   b) wife not discover us
3 not become / teacher   c) not find it difficult
4 have / car serviced   to give up
5 not start / smoking   d) not go in fancy dress
6 read / invitation   e) not marry him
                                  f) not break down

Now write conditional sentences to explain the regrets in more detail. Start with *If* ... . For two of the sentences, you will need to use a present tense in the second part of the sentence. Which ones?

Example: _If we hadn't gone to that bar, my wife_
          wouldn't have discovered us.

1 ....

2 ....

3 ....

4 ....

5 ....

Giving reasons

4 a) Fill in the gaps with *for / because / so that / because of / in order to / for*.

1 We came to this pub .... a quiet drink.

We came to this pub .... it's quiet.

We came to this pub .... nobody would see us.

2 I married him .... his power and influence.

I married him .... settle down and raise a family.

I married him .... I loved him.

3 I became a teacher .... I like working with children.

I became a teacher .... I could have a career I enjoyed.

I didn't become a teacher .... the money.

4 I bought this car .... my wife to use.

I bought this car .... it was cheap.

I bought this car .... get around.

b) Circle the correct ending for these sentences.

Example: 1 My wife discovered us even though
~~the fact that we came to this pub /~~
(we came to this pub.)

2 I love him despite **he's lazy / his laziness**.

3 I love teaching even though **it doesn't pay very well / the money**.

4 I love my car although **it keeps breaking down / the fact that it isn't reliable**.

c) Use the endings you didn't use in Exercise 4b), and complete the sentences.

Example: 1 My wife discovered us despite the fact that we came to this pub.

2 I love him ....

3 I love teaching, ...

4 I love my car ....

Reading: Meanings of *get*

5 a) Read the letter and decide if the sentences are true (T) or false (F). Write *T* or *F* in the boxes.

a) John doesn't know about the party. ☐

b) John is going to retire soon. ☐

c) June and April regularly communicate by e-mail. ☐

d) John is very skilled at using a computer. ☐

e) Tom and Jerry are probably April's sons. ☐

b) Look at the examples (1–12) of *get / getting* in the letter. Use a word from the Word Box to say what *get* means in each example.

receive	take	obtain
arrive		become

1 ....   7 ....

2 ....   8 ....

3 ....   9 ....

4 ....   10 ....

5 ....   11 ....

6 ....   12 ....

Dear June,

Sorry it's taken me so long to write back to you, but things have been getting [1] really hectic here. We're preparing, as you know, for John's retirement party, and it's going to be a big surprise. I hope he doesn't get [2] too much of a shock!

Twenty years with the same company! Can you imagine? The company is going to get [3] him a clock, and I think his colleagues are getting [4] him a set of golf clubs.

The children and I are getting [5] him a new computer, one with e-mail and the Internet! I know you've got one at home, so you'll be getting [6] e-mails from me from now on, rather than having to wait for a letter! Even though we're all getting [7] older, I don't think John'll find it too difficult to learn how to use one. He uses one a little at work, just for printing out invoices, but I'm sure he'll get [8] used to it.

I got a lovely postcard from Tom and Jerry in Greece. Tom said that they're getting [9] so tanned, you won't recognise them. When do they get [10] back?

Anyway, I'll finish now, because it's getting [11] late, and I have to get [12] the early train to Oxford tomorrow morning.

All my love,

April

Listening: Language of criticism

6 a) 🎧 (36) Carla doesn't get on with her brother Patrick. Listen, and decide if these sentences are true (T) or false (F). Write *T* or *F* in the boxes.

1 Patrick complains a lot. ☐
2 Patrick is sometimes asked to …
   a) take the dog for a walk. ☐
   b) do the washing up. ☐
   c) cook the dinner. ☐
3 Patrick sometimes borrows things which belong to Carla. ☐
4 He usually puts back the things he has borrowed. ☐
5 Patrick always asks if he can borrow Carla's bicycle. ☐
6 Patrick helps Carla with her homework. ☐
7 Carla's friends like Patrick a lot. ☐

b) 🎧 (36) Listen again, and complete these sentences.

1 He .... complaining.
2 He .... with the washing up.
3 He .... using my things.
4 I .... just taking them.
5 I .... not putting things back.
6 I .... a noise all the time.
7 He .... around shouting.

c) This is what Patrick thinks of Carla. Fill in the gaps with words from the Word Box.

⌜ fed up (x 2)   never   sick   always (x 2) ⌝

My sister Carla is horrible. She's ....(1) complaining about me! I'm ....(2) with her telling me that it's my turn to take the dog for a walk, and I'm ....(3) of her asking me to help with the washing up. She ....(4) lets me borrow her CDs, so I just take them anyway! She's ....(5) moaning about the noise I make; why can't she realise that boys are just noisier than girls! *And,* I'm ....(6) with her inviting her friends round.

What annoys people about their families? A survey of the top ten things which annoy us most.

1 Husbands who don't help with the housework.
2 Children who leave their homework until Sunday evening.
3 Wives who accuse their husbands of 'not listening'.
4 Husbands who don't want to talk about their feelings.
5 Brothers who borrow their sisters' CDs.
6 Teenagers who phone their friends all the time.
7 Wives who want to watch a film when there's football on the TV.
8 Fathers who tell awful jokes to their children's friends.
9 Teenagers who stay out too late.
10 Children who don't keep their bedrooms tidy.

7 Read the survey and complete these sentences using the words in brackets.

Example: 1 wife to husband
   (fed up / not help with housework)
I'm fed up with you not helping with the housework.

2 parent to child (always / leave homework until Sunday evening)

....

3 husband to wife (sick / accuse me / not listen)

....

4 wife to husband (never / want to talk / your feelings)

....

5 sister to brother (always / borrow my CDs / never / ask)

....

6 father to teenager
   (always / use the telephone / never / help to pay the bill)
.... ! ....

7 husband to wife (never / let me watch football)

....

8 teenager to father
   (fed up / you tell awful jokes / my friends)

....

9 mother to teenager (sick / you / come home late / never / tell me / where you're going)

.... ! ....

10 father to child (tired / tell you / tidy your room)

....

Question tags

8 a) Finish the statements with the correct question tags.

Example: You're my son's teacher, ...*aren't you?*...

1 You're my cousin's wife, ...?

2 You've had your hair cut, ...?

3 You can speak Japanese, ...?

4 You didn't drink my beer by mistake, ...?

5 You haven't seen my wife, ...?

6 You aren't the same Jay Hawkins I went to school with,

....?

7 I'm next, ...?

b) 👀 (37) Now listen and check.

c) 👀 (37) Listen again. Decide if the question tags are *R* (rising) or *F* (falling). Write *R* or *F* in the boxes.

1 ☐   2 ☐   3 ☐   4 ☐   5 ☐   6 ☐   7 ☐

The Great Grammar Giveaway!

9 Decide if these sentences are right or wrong. For each correct decision, you "win" £1,000. For each wrong decision, you "lose" £1,000. If you think a sentence is wrong, correct it. If your correction is correct, you "win" £1,000!

Sentences	Right	Wrong	Corrections
1 I shouldn't stay out so late last night. I'm tired!			
2 I don't think you should have asked the boss for more money. He looks angry!			
3 I wish I didn't meet you. You only make me sad.			
4 If only I sent the invitations for the party out on time! Nobody will come!			
5 If I sending the invitations out on time, everybody was coming. Now it's too late!			
6 If I hadn't asked the boss for more money, he wouldn't be angry.			
7 I wish I put on some warm clothes. I'm freezing!			
8 He's so annoying! He always asking me silly questions.			
9 I'm sick with you asking me silly questions all the time.			
10 You never doing the washing up! Why do I always have to do it?			
11 Even though you never buy me flowers, I still love you.			
12 I'm going to ask my boss for a holiday, because of I need a rest.			
	Number of correct decisions	**Number of correct decisions**	**Correct?**	
	£	£	£	Total £

Listening: "I love him, in spite of his bad points"

10 a) 👀 (38) **Read through questions 1–8 below. Then listen to the woman talking about a relationship. Choose the correct answer for each number.**

1 When they first met, the woman …
  a) had a busy life, but managed to spend a lot of time with him. ☐
  b) didn't have a busy life, and spent a lot of time with him. ☐
  c) had a busy life and didn't spend a lot of time with him. ☐

2 At that time she …
  a) regretted falling in love with him. ☐
  b) didn't regret falling in love with him. ☐
  c) didn't fall in love with him. ☐

3 She wanted them to be together because …
  a) she actually liked his bad points. ☐
  b) he was good to her, and showed her lots of affection. ☐
  c) he didn't have any bad points. ☐

4 Sometimes, he …
  a) watches too much television. ☐
  b) annoys her when she's watching television. ☐
  c) switches the television off. ☐

5 Sometimes, she …
  a) tells him to go out for the day. ☐
  b) goes out for the whole day. ☐
  c) doesn't know where he is. ☐

6 One day, he …
  a) rescued her from the sea. ☐
  b) nearly died in the sea. ☐
  c) rescued another person from the sea. ☐

7 When he was lost, she …
  a) thought horrible things about him. ☐
  b) regretted the horrible things she'd said to him. ☐
  c) said some horrible things to him. ☐

8 He is …
  a) a man with big, beautiful brown eyes. ☐
  b) a man with big, beautiful blue eyes. ☐
  c) a dog with big, beautiful brown eyes. ☐

b) 👀 (39) **Listen to the next part of the tape, and answer the question.**

Does the woman …
1 talk only about his good points?
2 talk about his irritating habits and his good points?
3 talk about more of his irritating habits?

c) 👀 (39) **What does he do? Listen again, and tick (✓) the correct sentences below.**

1 He chases the neighbours' cats. ☐
2 He chases people who live in the area. ☐
3 He tries to bite the postman. ☐
4 He eats too much food. ☐
5 He lies on the sofa or armchairs. ☐
6 He shakes water all over her when he's been out in the rain. ☐

Expressing regrets

d) Rewrite these sentences.

Example: I didn't give you a lot of attention.
    I should have given you more attention.

1 It was a bad idea to fall in love with you.

  I should ....

2 We met at the wrong time.

  If only ....

3 I wasn't very nice to you.

  If only ....

4 I wasn't at home very often.

  I wish ....

5 I didn't give you much affection.

  I should ....

Giving reasons and making contrasts

e) Use an item from each column to make four sentences about what you heard on the tape.

I wanted us to be together	although	his bad points.
	despite	the affection he shows me.
	because	he has some bad points.
	because of	he is affectionate.

1 ....
2 ....
3 ....
4 ....

Do you remember? Units 7–9

Past Perfect Simple or Past Simple?

1 **a)** Fill in the gaps with the correct form of the verbs in brackets.

What a terrible day I had yesterday! First, I (wake up) ....(1) late, because I (forget) ....(2) to set my alarm clock the night before. I (rush) ....(3) to the wardrobe to get my clothes out for work, but I realised I (not have) ....(4) a shirt, because I (forget) ....(5) to iron one. So, I quickly (iron) ....(6) one, got dressed, and left for work. When I (get) ....(7) to the station, I realised I (leave) ....(8) my season ticket at home. I didn't want to pay again, so I (go) ....(9) home and got it. Then when I (get back) ....(10) to the station, there was an announcement that the train (cancel)......................(11), so I had to wait half an hour for the next one. Finally, I (get) ....(12) to work. But there was nobody there! However, someone (leave) ....(13) a note for me on the door, to say that the heating (break down) ....(14), and so everyone (go) ....(15) home. It was nice to get the day off work, but I was feeling stressed anyway, because of my journey! So, I (go) ....(16) to a department store (to buy myself a new shirt), and then went home. However, when I got to my front door, I realised that I (not have) ....(17) my key! I tried to remember what I (do) ....(18) with it. Then I remembered. When I (go) ....(19) back home to get my season ticket, I (leave) ....(20) it on the cupboard in the kitchen ...

So and *because*

b) Complete these sentences with *so* or *because*.

Example: 1 I'd forgotten to set my alarm clock ...*so*... I woke up late.

2 I'd forgotten to iron a shirt, ... I didn't have one.

3 I had to wait half an hour .... the train was cancelled.

4 Everyone had gone home, ... the heating had broken down.

5 I'd left my key in the kitchen, ... I couldn't get in.

Reported Speech

2 Change the Reported Speech into Direct Speech, and the Direct Speech into Reported Speech.

1 "I've bought you some flowers!"

I told her ....

2 She said that she didn't really like them

....

3 I told her I'd bought her ones like that before.

....

4 "No you haven't! You're thinking of someone else!"

She said that .... , and that ....

....

Third Conditional

3 Write Third Conditional sentences based on these facts.

Example: Mario didn't study hard at school.
          He didn't pass his exams.
          If Mario had studied hard at school,
          he would have passed his exams.

1 Tracy forgot to tell Kevin about the party.
   He didn't know where it was.

   Kevin ....

2 I didn't know you were coming home early.
   I didn't make you anything to eat.

   If ....

3 I didn't eat any lunch.
   I was hungry all afternoon.

   I ....

4 You didn't give me proper directions.
   I didn't get there on time.

   If ....

Extend your reading Units 7–9

1 Are you addicted to the Internet? Read the article and find out.

Are You An Internet Addict?

Here are some key signs that your Internet use may be a problem. So you surf the Internet for an hour a day. OK, maybe for three hours, or five. At what point does this fascination become so compulsive that psychologists would call it an addiction?

Psychologist Kimberly S. Young, MD, PhD, founded the Center for On-Line Addiction[1] to help people with just this problem. She's identified eight key symptoms. Take a look at her list. If five or more apply, Young suggests you consider talking to a mental health professional about your Internet use.

1 *Preoccupation*
You think constantly about previous online activity or keep looking forward to the next online session. Some people crave time on the Internet the way a smoker craves a cigarette.

2 ....
You need to spend increasing amounts of time online to achieve satisfaction. A parent who's spending 50 hours a week in a chat room might neglect basic responsibilities such as doing the washing or cooking dinner for the children.

3 ....
You can't cut back on your Internet use, even after several attempts. Some people can't stop visiting chat rooms while at the office, even though they know their bosses are monitoring the sites they visit.

4 ....
You feel restless, moody, depressed, or irritable when you attempt to stop or cut down on Internet use. Some people feel so bad-tempered in jobs where they can't go online that they make excuses to go home and use the computer.

5 ....
Everyone lets time slip by occasionally while on the Internet, often surfing the web for hours on end. Consider it a problem if it happens to you consistently when you're online and you're also experiencing some of the other symptoms on this list.

6 ....
You jeopardise a significant relationship, job, or educational or career opportunity because of Internet use. One man decided to leave his wife of twenty-two years for someone he had corresponded with on the Internet for a couple of months.

7 ....
You lie to family members, a therapist, or others to conceal the extent of your involvement with the Internet. Someone who's seeing a therapist for depression might not tell the therapist about his/her Internet use.

8 ....
You use the Internet as a way to avoid thinking about problems, or to reduce depression or feelings of helplessness.

[1] http://www.netaddiction.com

2 Add the headings (a–j) to the paragraphs in the article. Look at the example. There are two extra headings.

a) Inability to stop
b) Escape
c) Lies
d) Loss of self-confidence
e) Withdrawal symptoms
f) Preoccupation ✓
g) Multiple addictions
h) Risky behaviour
i) Increased use
j) Lost sense of time

3 Choose the best ending for each sentence.

1 You might be addicted to the Internet if you ...
   a) really enjoy using it.
   b) get annoyed when you use it.
   c) need to use it to feel comfortable.

2 Some Internet addicts visit chat rooms at work ...
   a) in spite of knowing they shouldn't.
   b) because they know their boss isn't watching.
   c) in order to make useful work contacts.

3 When some addicts try to stop going online they ...
   a) feel worse.
   b) feel better.
   c) feel the same.

4 Some Internet addicts don't want to ...
   a) accept their responsibilities.
   b) admit their dependence on it.
   c) stay in their relationships.

5 If you're addicted to the Internet, you might lie about ...
   a) the websites you visit.
   b) the people you correspond with.
   c) the time you spend on it.

4 Match the words (1–8) to their meanings (a–h).

A	B
1 compulsive	a) want something extremely strongly
2 crave	b) having feelings that change easily and often
3 neglect	c) regularly
4 restless	d) hide
5 moody	e) to give too little care and attention to
6 jeopardise	f) impossible to stop or control
7 consistently	g) put something at risk or in danger
8 conceal	h) unable to keep still

5 Another form of communication is the mobile phone.
Before you read "Mobile phone facts" below, try to answer these questions.

1 Who has the highest number of mobile phone users in the world?　a) America ☐　b) China ☐　c) Japan ☐

2 How many people in the world have a mobile phone?　a) 150 million ☐　b) 350 million ☐　c) 550 million ☐

3 In the UK the busiest months on the network are …
　a) June and July. ☐　　b) August and September. ☐　　c) November and December. ☐

6 Now read the article and check your answers to Exercise 5.

Mobile phone facts

Britain has the fifth highest number of mobile phone users in the world after America, Japan, China and Italy. Finland, the home of Nokia, has the highest per capita use, where almost every household has a mobile phone.

About 24 million people in the UK have mobiles, and this number is expected to keep rising.

Around the world, about 350 million people are estimated to own one.

Busiest months on the network are November and December as families discuss arrangements for Christmas and businesses go through busy sales periods.

Thursday is the busiest day for calls in Britain. Nobody knows why. Between 4 p.m. and 5 p.m. is the busiest period as people try to finish work before clocking off, followed by between 10 a.m. and 11 a.m.

Special events push up the number of calls. At midnight on Millennium Eve, 13 million people tried to use their mobiles, causing a multi-network crash.

7 Read the article again and answer these questions.

1 What European country has the most mobile phones?
2 What will probably happen to the number of mobile phones in Britain?
3 What difference does Christmas make to the number of calls people make?
4 Why is Thursday the busiest day on the network?
5 What happened to the mobile phone networks in Britain on 31 December 1999? Why?

8 Complete these definitions with these words and phrases from the article You do not need one of them.

per capita	household	sign up	go through	clock off	push up

1 When you .... , you agree to a contract which obliges you to do something.

2 If you take the total amount of something in a country, and divide it by the number of people there, you get the

.... amount.

3 The group of people who live together in a house is called a ....

4 If you cause the amount or number of something to increase, you .... it ....

5 To .... , you record the time you stop work on a special card.

Extend your grammar Units 7–9

1 Here is an extract from *The Sound Machine*, a short story by Roald Dahl. Fill in the gaps with words from the Word Box. You don't need all the words.

> any   as   before   by   caught   felt
> going   him   if   into   it   itself   no
> of   once   one   so   suddenly   thing
> this   towards   where

He put his left hand on the controls and his right hand on the button that moved the needle across a large central dial, like the wavelength dial of a radio. The dial was marked with many numbers, starting at 15,000 and ....(1) on up to 1,000,000.

And now he was bending forward over the machine. The needle was travelling slowly across the dial, ...(2) slowly that he could hardly see it move, and in the earphones he could hear a faint noise.

Behind ....(3) noise, he could hear the sound of the machine itself, but that was all. ....(4) he listened, he became conscious ....(5) a strange feeling that his ears were stretching out away from his head. It ....(6) as if each ear were connected to his head ....(7) a thin stiff wire, and that the wires were getting longer, that his ears were going up and up ....(8) a secret and forbidden land, a dangerous world of sound ....(9) ears had never been before and had no right to be.

The needle moved slowly across the dial, and ....(10) he heard a scream, a terrible scream, and he jumped and ....(11) hold of the edge of the table. He looked quickly around him as if he expected to see the person who had screamed. There was ....(12)-one in sight except the woman in the garden next door, and she had not screamed. She was bending down, cutting yellow roses and putting them ....(13) her basket.

Again it came. A throatless, inhuman scream, sharp and short, very clear and cold. The note ....(14) had a hard metallic quality that he had never heard ....(15). Klausner looked around ....(16), trying to see where the noise had come from. The woman next door was the only living ....(17) in sight. He saw her reach down, take a rose stem in the fingers of ....(18) hand and cut the stem with a pair of scissors. ....(19) more he heard the scream. ....(20) came at the exact moment when the rose stem was cut.

2 Complete the second sentence using the words in capitals so that it means the same as the first sentence.

Example: The question was so difficult that I couldn't answer it.
SUCH
It was ...*such a difficult question that I*... couldn't answer it.

1 The operator asked me to hold the line so that he could put me through.
TO
The operator asked me to hold ....
.... through.

2 Last Saturday, my closest friend got married.
WHO
The person ....
.... my closest friend.

3 I doubt if I'll have time to scan all these photos.
LIKELY
I'm .... time to scan all these photos.

4 In the past, people used to believe that the earth was flat.
BELIEVED
In the past, the earth .... be flat.

5 "I'll definitely call home if there is any problem," Megan said.
PROMISED
Megan .... any problem.

6 People in Europe used to have more children years ago.
MANY
People in Europe ....
they used to.

7 I didn't know you had to send a fax, so I didn't offer you the use of my fax machine.
WOULD
If I ....
.... the use of my fax machine.

8 It would have been a good idea to leave a message on the answerphone.
SHOULD
We ....
on the answerphone.

Extend your writing Units 7–9

1 a) Read the story below, ignoring the spaces. Underline the correct tense in the brackets. The first one has been done as an example.

Can you give me a lift?

At 10 o'clock on a .... November evening in downtown Seattle, a .... woman (returned / <u>was returning</u>)[1] to her car when a .... man (had come / came)[2] and spoke to her. At the time she (felt / was feeling)[3] rather afraid because she (just saw / had just seen)[4] a .... horror movie.

The man (was explaining / explained)[5] that earlier that evening he (was seeing / had seen)[6] some .... children around her car and (was deciding / had decided)[7] to look after it for her. He (had said / said)[8] that .... because of this, he (was missing / had missed)[9] the last train home. He .... (asked / was asking)[10] her for a lift home. At first she .... (had felt / felt)[11] a bit worried but after a few moments, she .... (was agreeing / agreed)[12].

It (was / had been)[13] a .... cold night but she .... (was noticing / noticed)[14] sweat on his face and she (had started / started)[15] to worry. Why (was he / had he been)[16] so .... nervous? ...., she (asked / was asking)[17] him to get out of the car and direct her out of the parking lot. As he .... (showed / was showing)[18] her the way out, she (was driving / drove)[19] away .... leaving him behind.

Ten minutes later, after she (calmed / had calmed)[20] down, she (was noticing / noticed)[21] that he (left / had left)[22] his .... briefcase on the floor of the car. She (was stopping / stopped)[23] and, ... , (opened / was opening)[24] it. Inside, as she (was looking / looked)[25] through his books and papers, ... she (found / had found)[26] a long knife with a bloody blade!

b) Read the story again. This time, choose one of the expressions from the Word Box below to fill in the spaces in the story and make it more dramatic and interesting. Use your dictionary if necessary.

> spine-chilling   unfortunately   hesitantly   at high speed   nervously   suspicious-looking
> bitterly   battered   shaking with fear   to her horror   attractive   young   understandably
> suddenly   obviously   politely   gloomy   handsome   alarmed   carefully

10 What's going on?

There's a riot going on

1 Read the clues, and put the words in the wall. The letters on the shaded bricks make a word. What is it?

1 To enter without permission, using force (verb)
2 Physical force which can injure or cause damage. (noun)
3 To steal things from shops (etc.) usually when there's a (4) going on. (verb)
4 A social disturbance, often involving (2). (noun)
5 The people who the police think are responsible for a crime. (noun)

6 To demonstrate against something you disagree with. (verb)
7 To destroy something completely, usually a place or an object. (verb)
8 To use (2) against someone who is also using it against you. (verb)
9 What the police do if they catch a (5). (verb)
10 To throw something using a lot of strength.

The Passive

2 a) Fill in the gaps to complete these news stories using the verbs from the Word Boxes. Use the correct tense, and the correct passive or active form.

> see   beat   give

1 World famous football team Tadchester City ....(1) yesterday by a team from the village of Bottomley. Tadchester City star player Danny Beckenham said it was unfair that Bottomley ....(2) a penalty two minutes from the end of the match. He also said that he ....(3) Bottomley player Ted Farmer give the referee some money before the match.

> use   invent   buy   retire   go up

2 Top computer company Macrostuff ....(1) yesterday by the billionaire media tycoon Robert Mardock for $20 billion. The value of Macrostuff ....(2) by 20 per cent, and the founder of the company, William Dawes, ...(3), saying he is looking forward to never working again. Dawes ....(4) the computer programme "Fenestro", which ....(5) on most of the world's personal computers.

> take   throw   injure

3 Singing star Alvin Parsley ....(1) last night when an item of women's clothing ....(2) onto the stage during a concert. The clothing landed on Parsley's head, and he was unable to see properly. A member of the audience ....(3) to hospital also, after the singer landed on her when he fell off the stage.

> notice   release   find

4 Famous criminal Violet Crabbe ....(1) from prison yesterday after thirty years. Crabbe and her sister Veronica were imprisoned for their part in The Great Bus Robbery, and for the murder of their friend Jackie "the Bump" Rowntree. Rowntree's body ....(2) under a motorway, when drivers ....(3) that the surface of the road wasn't flat.

b) 🔊 (40) Now listen and check.

Who did it?

c) Look back at Exercise 2a), and tick (✓) the correct answer for these questions.

1 Which team won the football match?
 a) Tadchester City ☐
 b) Bottomley ☐

2 Who gave Bottomley a penalty near the end of the match?
 a) Danny Beckenham ☐
 b) The referee ☐

3 Who bought Macrostuff for $20 billion?
 a) Robert Mardock ☐
 b) William Dawes ☐

4 Who uses "Fenestro" on their computers?
 a) Everybody in the world ☐
 b) Most people who own a computer ☐

5 Who threw something onto the stage during Alvin's concert?
 a) A member of the audience ☐
 b) Alvin Parsley ☐

6 Who / What probably took the injured member of the audience to hospital?
 a) Alvin Parsley ☐
 b) An ambulance ☐

7 Who found Jackie "the Bump" Rowntree's body?
 a) The police ☐
 b) The Crabbe sisters ☐

8 Who told police that the road wasn't flat?
 a) Drivers ☐
 b) The Crabbe sisters ☐

d) Look back at Exercise 2c), and complete these sentences using the Past Simple passive form. Only use "by ..." where it is necessary.

Examples: The football match *was won by Bottomley.* (win)

Bottomley *were given a penalty* near the end of the match (give / a penalty)

1 Macrostuff .... for $20 billion. (buy)

2 "Fenestro" .... (use)

3 Something .... during Alvin's concert. (throw / onto the stage)

4 The injured member of the audience ....
 .... (take / to hospital)

5 Jackie "the Bump" Rowntree's body
 ....
 .... (find)

6 The police ....
 (tell / the road wasn't flat)

Listening: "It wasn't me"

3 a) 〔OO〕 (41) **Listen to Violet Crabbe talking about her life, and put these events in the right order. Number them 1–11. Write any dates you hear in the spaces.**

☐ She came out of prison.

☐ A gang of criminals carried out the Great Bus Robbery. ....

☐ She went to Parkville prison. ....

☐ The police arrested Violet. She went to prison for the murder. ....

☐ First arrested by police: aged 16; crime: stealing sweets

☐1 Date of Birth: *July 31st, 1945*

☐ She left Ardnock school.

☐ Veronica Crabbe helped her to escape from prison.
 ....

☐ Her autobiography (*It wasn't me*) comes out.

☐ Someone killed Jackie "the Bump" Rowntree.
 ....

☐ The police arrested her, and accused her of organising the robbery. ....

b) Use the information in brackets to write passive sentences about Violet Crabbe.

Example: *She was born on the 31st of July 1945.*
 (to be born / 31st July 1945)

1 ....
 (arrest / first time / 16 years old)

2 ....
 (arrest / 1971 / accuse / organising the Great Bus robbery)

3 ....
 (help / to escape / her sister Veronica)

4 ....
 (release / from prison / last week)

5 ....
 (her autobiography / release / next week)

The Passive: *to be*, *be*, or *being*?

4 **a)** Fill in the gaps in these passive sentences with *to be* / *be* / *being*, and the correct form of the verb in brackets.

1 The company sales figures will .... next month. (release)

2 He should .... that the company is doing badly. (tell)

3 Jane would appreciate .... to speak at the conference. (invite)

4 Would you prefer .... a bunch of flowers or a big bar of chocolate? (give)

5 I don't like .... flowers. They always make me sneeze! (give)

6 He doesn't want .... while he's working. (disturb)

7 The company paid for her .... as a computer programmer. (train)

8 Students should .... to use the passive only when it is appropriate. (encourage)

The Passive: *Get*

b) The famous criminal Violet Crabbe has led a violent life. Read this short extract from her autobiography *It wasn't me*. Fill in the gaps using the verbs in the Word Box and the *get* passive.

It wasn't me
by Violet Crabbe

| trap | hurt | arrest | knock | wreck | hit |

When I .... [1], I was in a pub called *The Deaf Beggar's Arms*, and there was a lot of shouting and fighting when the police came in. I think a policeman .... [2] by a handbag. I didn't do it, though; it wasn't me! There were a lot of people there, and I .... [3] in the middle, and I couldn't run anywhere. My sister Veronica .... [4] down by a policeman, and the whole pub .... [5]. I didn't break anything, though. It wasn't me! A lot of people .... [6] for no reason. It was all so unnecessary. And I lost my handbag somewhere ...

Passive with indirect objects

c) Write passive sentences to show what is happening in the pictures.

Example: 1 *I was told to come and see you.*

2 ....

3 ....

4 ....

It's a crime!

5 Read the sentences and rewrite the crime words.

1 knird gnivrid
2 dlingdif spexesen
3 poshtlingfi
4 rugbylar
5 regyrof
6 dufar

1 He went to the pub and then went home by car.

....

2 She got money from her company for lunches she didn't have. ....

3 He stole things from a shop. ....

4 He broke into a house and stole the TV. ....

5 She made £100 notes on her computer. ....

6 She used another person's credit card to pay for a holiday. ....

Negative questions

6 a) Write negative questions using the ideas below, then match the questions (1–7) and answers (a–g).

1 want / some more / cake

 Don't you want some more cake?

2 you / not / frighten / by the film

 ....?

3 we / meet / somewhere / before

 ....?

4 should / you / be at work

 ....?

5 she / famous film star

 ....?

6 we / saw / that man / on TV yesterday

 ....?

7 you / were / my teacher

 ....?

a) Ten years ago, at that school in Santiago.

b) She was in *Pass the Salt*.

c) No thanks, I'm full.

d) His photograph was on the news.

e) I've got the day off.

f) It wasn't very scary at all!

g) Last night, at the club.

Pronunciation: stress in negative questions

b) 🎧 (42) Listen to the negative questions from Exercise 6a). Underline the final stressed syllable on each negative question you wrote. From the beginning of the sentence to the final stressed syllable, what does the speaker's voice do? (The answer is the same for all of them.)

a) go up and down a lot   b) stay level   c) start really high and end up low   d) start really low and end up high

Laws, rules and social behaviour

7 a) Use words from both Word Boxes to make sentences using an infinitive.

> illegal   rude   against the rules

> smoke in this building   murder
> point at people   burgle a house
> belch after a meal   pick your nose in public
> take flash photos in the theatre
> watch adult films if you aren't 18 ✓

Example: It's illegal <u>to watch</u> adult films if you aren't 18.

1 ....

2 ....

3 ....

4 ....

5 ....

6 ....

7 ....

b) Rewrite the sentences from Exercise 7a). Use verb + *-ing* and an appropriate word from the Word Box.

> against the law   not allowed to   anti-social

Example: Watching adult films if you aren't 18 is against the law.

1 ....

2 ....

3 ....

4 ....

5 ....

6 ....

7 ....

Listening: Strange Laws

a

b

c

d

GIVE WAY

e

f

g

beard licence

h

8 **a)** In which pictures (a–h) can you find these things?

1 A moose ☐   5 Someone who is scruffy ☐
2 A bear ☐   6 A goatee beard ☐
3 A toilet ☐   7 A place of execution ☐
4 An alligator ☐   8 Someone eating ice cream ☐

b) 🔘 (43) Listen to the radio programme about strange laws. Match these place names (1–8) to the pictures (a–h).

Place	Goes with picture
1 Alaska (Fairbanks)	☐
2 Alaska (no town or city mentioned)	☐
3 Britain	☐
4 Greece	☐
5 Massachusetts (USA)	☐
6 Michigan (USA)	☐
7 Ottawa (Canada)	☐
8 Singapore	☐

c) 🔘 (43) **Read the questions below. Then listen again, and circle the correct answer.**

1 In Greece, you can **go to prison / be fined** for driving in scruffy clothes.

2 In Fairbanks you **must / can't** let moose walk on the pavement.

3 In Singapore, you can **be fined / go to prison** for not flushing the toilet.

4 Children in Ottawa **can't / can only** eat ice cream on Sundays.

5 In Alaska, you **can't / must** wake up a sleeping bear.

6 You **can't / must** tie your alligator to a fire hydrant in Michigan.

7 You **need / don't need** a licence in Massachusetts for all types of beard.

8 An old British law meant you could be **executed / fined** for trying to kill yourself.

d) **Use the words in brackets to rewrite these sentences.**

Example: It is illegal to drive while wearing scruffy clothes in Greece. (against the law)

It is *against the law to drive while wearing scruffy clothes in Greece.*

1 It is illegal in Fairbanks to let a moose walk on the pavement. (against the law)

It ....

2 It is illegal not to flush the toilet in Singapore. (must)

You ....

3 You can't eat ice cream on a Sunday in Ottawa. (not allowed)

Eating ....

4 It is against the law to wake up a sleeping bear in Alaska. (illegal)

Waking ....

5 You aren't allowed to tie an alligator to a fire hydrant in Michigan. (mustn't)

You ....

6 You must have a licence if you want to wear a goatee beard in Massachusetts. (against the law)

Wearing .... without ....

7 It used to be against the law in Britain to kill yourself. (illegal)

Killing ....

At the cinema

1 a) Label the diagram using the words in the Word Box. Then fill in the gaps.

| front row | screen | audience | seat | aisle | foyer | back row | usher |

I love going to the cinema. The first thing I do is buy a fizzy drink and some popcorn in the ....(1). Then after the ....(2) has shown me to my ....(3), I sit back to enjoy the experience. I never sit in the ....(4), because it's too near the ....(5). When I was a teenager, I always used to sit in the ....(6) with my girlfriend, but now I like to sit in the middle, near the ....(7). That's because if there's someone in the ....(8) with a large hat, I can still see the film!

b) Fill in the gaps using the correct form of the words in the Word Box.

| romantic | critics | dub | direct | special effects | thriller | stunt | star | black and white |
| subtitles | versions | set | commercial | actress | make |

My favourite film is called *Rocky Island*. It's a ....(1) film, and it was ....(2) in 1952. It ....(3) the American actor Dirk Stroganoff and the French–Canadian ....(4) Candide Demure. It's ....(5) on a small island off the coast of Florida, just after the Second World War.

It was ....(6) by Burt Madison, who also made *Rocky Island II: Love on the rocks*. It was a big ....(7) success at the time, and many film ....(8) still say it is one of the best films ever made. There aren't many ....(9), but Dirk Stroganoff did all his own ....(10). There aren't any car chases, because it's set on a small island, and there weren't many roads there; I suppose it's more of a psychological ....(11), as there is a murder involved, but it's also a very ....(12) film, as the two main characters fall in love. Since then, it's been ....(13) into about fourteen different languages, and there are other ....(14) in English, but with ....(15).

c) 👀 (44) Now listen and check.

All, whole, every

2 Fill in the gaps with *all / every / whole*.

1 .... time we get together, we talk about our favourite films.

2 Yes, we talk about films .... the time.

3 Sometimes we spend the .... evening talking about films.

4 Once, we spent the .... day at the cinema.

5 I know .... film that Dirk Stroganoff has been in.

6 I've followed his .... career.

Reading: Robert De Niro

3 **a)** Read the text about Robert De Niro, and choose the best title (a–f) for each paragraph (1–6).

a) A famous collaboration   b) Why is he such a good actor?   c) Awards

d) His later career   e) What type of characters has he played?   f) Who is he?

1) ....

Robert De Niro, who is considered one of the greatest actors of his generation, was born in New York in 1943. He has been an actor for his whole adult life, and he has managed to portray a range of fascinating characters, while mostly keeping his private life out of the news.

2) ....

He is renowned for his thorough preparation for every role he takes. For example, in the film *Raging Bull* (1980), in which he plays real-life boxer turned nightclub owner Jake La Motta, De Niro trained hard in order to get the physique of a boxer. In later life, La Motta put on a lot of weight, and so De Niro put on nearly twenty kilos for this part of the film.

3) ....

Raging Bull was directed by Martin Scorsese, and in all the films they have made together, they have rarely failed to achieve both critical and commercial success. Other successful films they have made together include *Mean Streets* (1973) and *New York, New York* (1977).

4) ....

In many of his films, De Niro plays people who are emotionally troubled, and who are prone to physical violence. The best-known examples are *Taxi Driver* (1976) and *Goodfellas* (1990). One of his most frightening roles was that of Max Cady in *Cape Fear* (1992), where the character takes revenge on a lawyer who failed to prevent him from going to prison. However, not all his films are violent, and he has made other films where he plays honest and virtuous members of the community.

5) ....

De Niro won an Oscar for best supporting actor in 1974 for the mostly Italian-speaking role of Vito Corleone in *The Godfather, Part II.* He also won the Academy Award for best actor in *Raging Bull* (1980), and was nominated as best actor for his roles in *Taxi Driver* (1976), *The Deer Hunter* (1978), and *Cape Fear* (1992).

6) ....

In 1988, De Niro set up his own film production company, TriBeCa films, based in New York, and began both producing and directing films, as well as continuing to act. Some of his more recent films haven't been so successful, and he took on roles which critics thought weren't as powerful as those for which he became famous. For example, in 2000, he made *Rocky and Bullwinkle*, a version of a 1960s American cartoon, which mixed live acting with animation. The film was not a big success at the box office. Nevertheless, although he has made one or two unsuccessful films, most filmgoers agree that he has a remarkable talent.

b) Decide if these sentences are true (T) or false (F). Write *T* or *F* in the boxes.

1 Robert De Niro has been an actor all his adult life. ☐

2 People know a lot about his private life. ☐

3 He puts a lot of work into preparing for films. ☐

4 He hasn't made many violent films. ☐

5 He stopped acting when he set up TriBeCa films. ☐

6 Many people think his earlier films are better than his more recent ones. ☐

c) Find words / expressions in the text which are alternatives to the underlined words.

Example: *Taxi Driver* is <u>thought of</u> as one of De Niro's best films. (Paragraph 1) *considered*

1 In *Cape Fear*, De Niro <u>plays</u> Max Cady. (Paragraph 1) ....

2 In *The Godfather, Part II*, De Niro played the <u>part</u> of Vito Corleone. (Paragraph 2) ....

3 *Goodfellas* was a <u>box office hit</u>. (Paragraph 3) ....

4 De Niro is <u>not the main character</u> in many of his films. (Paragraph 5) ....

Reporting verbs

4 **a)** Complete the table using an appropriate reporting verb from the Word Box.

> want ✓   tell   ask   promise   refuse   agree   warn   offer   refuse   ask

Direct Speech	Reported Speech
Example: I wish that man would stop talking. I can't hear the film	(S)he wanted the man to stop talking.
1 Excuse me, could you please stop talking? I can't hear the film.	(S)he .... him to stop talking.
2 Look. Just stop talking. OK?	(S)he .... him to stop talking.
3 Listen. If you don't stop talking, I'll ask the manager to throw you out.	(S)he .... him to stop talking.
4 Please, Jake. I don't want any trouble. Will you just get off my land?	Luke .... Jake to leave.
5 I'm staying right here, Luke. I'm not going anywhere.	Jake .... to go.
6 Look, if you go, I'll give you all my cows.	Luke .... to give Jake his cows.
7 I'm not going unless you give me all your cows, and let me take Maria, too.	Jake .... to go unless Luke lets him take Maria, too.
8 OK, if you promise to look after her.	Luke .... to let Jake take Maria.
9 Don't worry. I'll take good care of her.	Jake .... to take care of her.

b) 🔊 (45) Listen to this extract from the film *Cowboys of the Canyon*. Decide if these sentences are true (T) or false (F). Write *T* or *F* in the boxes.

1 Maria wants Jake to shoot Luke. ☐
2 Jake refuses to do what she wants. ☐
3 Jake agrees to do what Maria wants if she agrees to marry him. ☐
4 Maria refuses to marry Jake. ☐
5 Jake offers to take her to California. ☐
6 Maria refuses to go with him. ☐

c) Correct these sentences. Use the Past Simple tense.

Example:
Maria wanted that Jake should leave Luke in peace.
Maria wanted Jake to leave Luke in peace.

1 Jake promised leave Luke in peace if Maria married him.

....

2 Jake wanted that Maria should marry him.

....

3 Maria is agreed marry him.

....

4 Jake want that she go to California with him.

....

5 Maria was want a big wedding with all her relatives.

....

So and *such*

5 Fill in the gaps with *so / such / such a.*

1 The film was .... boring that I fell asleep in the middle.

2 It was .... boring film that I fell asleep in the middle.

3 He plays .... realistic characters.

4 The character he plays is .... realistic.

5 The special effects in the film are .... spectacular!

6 I've never seen .... spectacular special effects!

7 She's .... talented director! And her films are .... beautiful!

8 There aren't many directors who have .... talent! And there aren't many who make .... beautiful films, either.

Permission and requests

6 a) Decide if the sentences on the left are asking for permission (P) or requests (R). Write *P* or *R* in the boxes.

R 1 Would you mind opening the door for me?	a) Certainly, madam. Here you are.
☐ 2 Do you mind if I open the window?	b) Not at all. Allow me.
☐ 3 Could I have two first class stamps, please?	c) Sorry. I'm afraid it isn't free.
☐ 4 Could you put me through to Mr Timpkins?	d) Of course not. Please go ahead.
☐ 5 Is it all right if I sit here?	e) Certainly, madam. Please hold the line.
☐ 6 Could I have that blue armchair over there?	f) Sure. Go ahead.
☐ 7 Can I use your phone, John?	g) But I don't even know you!
☐ 8 Do you mind if I use your mobile phone, madam?	h) Certainly. Are you paying by credit card?

Now match the sentences (1–8) to the correct response (a–h).

b) 📼 (46) Now listen and check.

Giving and Refusing Permission

7 a) Fill in the gaps with *Yes / No*.

1 Would you mind opening the door for me? ...., not at all.

2 Can I borrow your pen? ...., go ahead.

3 Excuse me, is anyone sitting here? ...., I'm afraid it's taken.

4 Do you mind if I open the window? ...., of course not.

5 Can I open the window? ...., please do.

6 Is it all right if I sit here? ...., please go ahead.

7 Do you mind if I borrow your pen? ...., of course not.

8 Could I possibly borrow your pen? ...., of course.

b) Tick (✓) the answers in Exercise 8a) which give permission.

c) Underline the syllables in the questions in Exercise 7a) which are stressed the most.

d) 📼 (47) Now listen and check.

e) 📼 (47) Listen again. Are the questions said politely (P) or impolitely (I)?

8 a) Match the requests (1–6) to the refusals (a–f).

1 Do you mind if I smoke?	a) I'd prefer it if you didn't. I'm feeling cold.
2 Could I possibly borrow £10,000?	b) Actually, I was going to use it myself.
3 Is it okay if I sit here?	c) I'd prefer it if you didn't. It makes me cough.
4 Do you mind if I open the window?	d) I'm afraid he's hurt his leg.
5 Do you mind if I dance with your husband?	e) I'm afraid it's taken.
6 Can I borrow your car, Dad?	f) I'm afraid I can't authorise any more lending.

b) 📼 (48) Now listen and check.

"Can I borrow your car, Dad?"

Reading: Hammer Horror

9 **a)** **Read the introduction and choose the best way to complete the sentence.**

1 Hammer studios made …
   a) only horror films. ☐
   b) horror films and other types of film, too. ☐
   c) films about graveyards. ☐
2 Hammer horror films are …
   a) very different from most horror films. ☐
   b) typical of what many people think of as horror films. ☐
   c) the same as all other horror films. ☐
3 Compared with today's horror films, some people think that …
   a) Hammer films may look old, and not very frightening. ☐
   b) Hammer films are much more frightening. ☐
   c) Hammer make other types of film, too. ☐

It is a cold, dark stormy night, and you are lost, stumbling through a graveyard. Bats fly overhead, and the clouds race past the moon. You hear a creaking noise, and suddenly a hand reaches out from a grave and grabs your ankle … These are typical images from the series of horror films made by Hammer Films, mostly during the 1950s, 60s and 70s. Hammer made other types of films too, but it was their horror films which became the studio's best-known product. Their most famous and most successful films were directed by Terence Fisher, and starred Christopher Lee and Peter Cushing.

The films are a good demonstration of what most people consider to be archetypal horror films, with lots of gothic castles, graveyards, and, of course, plenty of blood, too. Although some people may consider them a little dated, and mild by today's horror standards, they were considered gory and very frightening in their time. Here are three reviews of some of Hammer's best-known films.

The Curse of Frankenstein (1957)
Directed by Terence Fisher
Starring Peter Cushing as Baron Frankenstein and Christopher Lee as the Creature

Based on the classic novel by Mary Shelley, this is for many people a seminal horror movie, in a style which has influenced other films in the genre ever since. The film begins with the words "More than a hundred years ago, in a mountain village in Switzerland, lived a man whose strange experiments with the dead have since become legend." This is our introduction to Baron Frankenstein, who makes a creature from parts of bodies stolen from graves. His experiments have horrific consequences, as in creating a physical life, he has inadvertently made a misunderstood creature who only seeks company and a spiritual life.

Dracula (1958)
Directed by Terence Fisher
Starring Peter Cushing as Professor Van Helsing, Christopher Lee as Count Dracula, and John van Eyssen as Jonathan Harker

The original novel by Bram Stoker provided the inspiration for another successful horror film from Hammer studios. After a difficult journey, Jonathan Harker arrives at the remote Castle Dracula in the Carpathian Mountains. He has been asked there to index the library belonging to the aristocratic Count Dracula. However, Harker also knows that the Count is a 400-year-old vampire, who feasts on the blood of his victims, and plans to kill him. There are unfortunate consequences for Harker, as the Count falls in love with a photograph of his girlfriend, and plans to find her. Harker asks Professor van Helsing to help him, as the professor is the only one who knows enough about vampires …

The Hound of the Baskervilles (1958)
Directed by Terence Fisher
Starring Peter Cushing as Sherlock Holmes, Andre Morell as Dr Watson, and Christopher Lee as Sir Henry Baskerville

Based on Sir Arthur Conan Doyle's famous Sherlock Holmes novel, this atmospheric film tells the story of Sir Henry Baskerville, who inherits the family property in a wild and lonely place when his relative, Sir Charles Baskerville, dies in mysterious circumstances. He decides to investigate the legend of the hound from Hell who, it is said, brings death to each head of the Baskerville family. After a series of strange and terrifying events, he calls in Sherlock Holmes to help. Sherlock Holmes is unable to go, and so he asks his friend Dr Watson to accompany Sir Henry …

---

b) **Read the information about the films, and answer the questions.**

1 Who wrote the novel *Frankenstein*? ....

2 In which country is *The Curse of Frankenstein* set?

....

3 Why was Jonathan Harker invited to Castle Dracula?

....

4 Who does Count Dracula try to find? ....

5 Who knows more about vampires than Jonathan Harker?

....

6 Who inherits the Baskerville family property?

....

7 Who brings death to each head of the Baskerville family?

....

⑫ Taking off

Favourite holidays

1 **a)** Fill in the gaps using words from the Word Box. You may need to change the form of the verbs.

> great nightlife   chilled out   work my way
> souvenirs   off the beaten track
> take risks   see the sights   on a budget

1 My favourite holiday was in Paris, a couple of years ago. I really love .... We went to the Eiffel Tower, the Louvre, the Arc de Triomphe. We saw everything! I love buying ...., too. I got a lovely little model of the Eiffel Tower. I gave it to my mother.

2 I went to Ibiza last year, and had a great time! There's such .... there that I didn't actually see much of the place we stayed in! We went clubbing all night, and just .... in the day in the hotel. We were ...., so we couldn't do anything too expensive. We saved our money for the clubs.

3 I'm going to .... round South America. I've taken a course in how to teach English, and I'm going to use that to help me travel. I'm going to go to unusual places, a bit .... I don't like places where you just meet lots of people from your own country. I want to ...., and live a little dangerously.

b) 👓 (49) **Now listen and check.**

Reading: Does travelling make you sick?

For a long time, doctors have been trying to understand why some people feel ill when they travel long distances, and others don't. The effects are the same, whether you're travelling by car, ship or plane; you feel dizzy, your mouth feels dry, you feel as though you're going to faint, and often all of these lead to vomiting. Travel-sickness pills can help to take away the feeling of nausea, but the best remedies are a combination of experience and common sense.

If you're travelling by car, first of all make sure there is plenty of air. Open a window, or turn the air-conditioning on. Also, if you're a passenger, it's a good idea to focus on things in the distance. Lots of us like to read while travelling in the car, but trying to keep your eyes on the page, as it moves with the car, can increase the feeling of sickness.

On an aeroplane, the best advice is to avoid alcohol. Not only can too much make you feel sick, but also in the pressurised air of the cabin, its effects are increased. Drink plenty of water, instead, as you tend to get dehydrated on long flights.

When travelling by ship, it's difficult to avoid the swaying motion, but if you are feeling sick, the effects of the movement will be less if you sit down. Again it's a good idea to avoid too much alcohol, and steer clear of rich food, also. Bon Voyage!

2 **Read the article and choose the best answer from the choices below.**

1 Doctors …
  a) know why some people get travel sick and others don't. ☐
  b) don't know why some people get travel sick and others don't. ☐
  c) think they know why some people get travel sick. ☐

2 If you're travelling by car, you should …
  a) shut all the windows and stare at your fingers, or read a book. ☐
  b) open a window, look into the distance and not try to read. ☐
  c) sway from side to side as the car moves along. ☐

3 If you're travelling by plane, you should …
  a) take some advice. ☐
  b) spend a couple of hours drinking beer in the airport bar before your flight. ☐
  c) not drink alcohol, and drink lots of water instead. ☐

4 If you're travelling by ship, you should …
  a) avoid other passengers. ☐
  b) sit in the café with a beer and a cream cake. ☐
  c) sit down, and avoid alcohol and rich food. ☐

Present deductions

3 a) Mary and Trevor have booked a hotel, but they aren't sure which one is theirs.
Write sentences for each hotel. Choose from the reasons given in the box.

> there is a restaurant next door ✓   there is / isn't a swimming pool on the roof   it isn't family-run
> it doesn't look very friendly   it isn't finished yet   it begins with a 'B'

1 Hotel Berlin

Example: It could be the Hotel Berlin,
because there is a restaurant next door.

It can't be the Hotel Berlin, ...

2 Hotel Bueno
It might be the Hotel Bueno ....

It can't be the Hotel Bueno, ...

3 Hotel Bali
It might not be the Hotel Bali, ...

It could be the Hotel Bali ....

and ....

4 Hotel Biarritz
It can't be the Hotel Biarritz, ...

It might be the Hotel Biarritz, because

.... !

b) ◉◉ (50) Now listen and check.

c) ◉◉ (50) Listen again. Write *M* (Mary) or *T* (Trevor).

Who thinks:
1 it could be the Hotel Berlin? ☐
2 it can't be the Hotel Berlin? ☐
3 it might be the Hotel Bueno? ☐
4 it can't be the Hotel Bueno? ☐
5 it could be the Hotel Bali? ☐
6 it can't be the Hotel Bali? ☐
7 it might be the Hotel Biarritz? ☐
8 it can't be the Hotel Biarritz? ☐
9 they must be in the wrong town? ☐

Listening: What on earth is it?

a)
b)
c)
d)

4 **a)** 🎧 (51) **Listen to this radio programme.**

1 Is the programme about strange objects?
  Yes ☐   No ☐
2 Which object is being described?
  a ☐   b ☐   c ☐   d ☐

b) 🎧 (51) **Listen again and decide if the sentences are true (T) or false (F). Write *T* or *F* in the boxes.**

1 If you want to see the objects on the show, you have to visit the radio station. ☐
2 Sir Arthur Expert thinks the object might be from South London. ☐
3 He thinks that it might be a musical instrument. ☐
4 The presenter thinks Sir Arthur might have broken it. ☐
5 Sir Arthur suggests that it might have been used in wedding ceremonies. ☐
6 He thinks that it must be a stool for short men to stand on. ☐

Pronunciation

5 **a)** **Underline the main stressed syllables in the following dialogues.**

Example: A: It <u>might</u> be a musical instrument.
B: It <u>can't</u> be a musical instrument. It doesn't make any <u>noise</u>.

1 A: He must be Spanish.
  B: He can't be Spanish. He's got blue eyes!
2 A: It could be a kind of chair.
  B: It can't be a kind of chair. It's really uncomfortable!
3 A: They might have gone on holiday.
  B: They can't have gone on holiday. I saw them an hour ago.
4 A: They can't be married!
  B: They must be. They're wearing rings.
5 A: She could have gone to the shops.
  B: She can't have gone to the shops. She's left the door open!

b) 🎧 (52) **Now listen and check.**

Corrections: Making deductions

6 **a)** **Tick (✓) the sentences which are correct, and put a cross (✗) by the ones which are wrong.**

1 They can't be at home, because the lights aren't switched on. ☐
2 This must be the right key. We've tried all the others! ☐
3 You might not be hungry! You've just eaten everything in the fridge! ☐
4 John must have been hungry. He ate everything in the fridge. ☐
5 I don't know what it is. It can be a musical instrument, or it can be a chair. ☐
6 It mustn't be a chair! It looks really uncomfortable. ☐

b) **Now write corrections for the three sentences that were wrong in Exercise 6a).**

a) ....

b) ....

c) ....

Present and Past

c) **Match the sentences (1–8) with the meanings (a–h).**

1 It must be true.
2 It can't be true.
3 It might be true.
4 It might not be true.
5 It must have been true.
6 It can't have been true.
7 It might have been true.
8 It might not have been true.

a) I think it was possibly true.
b) I think it possibly wasn't true.
c) I'm sure it was true.
d) I'm sure it wasn't true.
e) I think it's possibly true.
f) I think it possibly isn't true.
g) I'm sure it's true.
h) I'm sure it isn't true.

d) **Fill in the gaps using the modal verbs from the box.**

| must   can't   might |

Example: They *can't have* bought a cat.
Trevor hates having animals in the house.

1 He .... taken his car. Here are his car keys.

2 He .... gone by train. I think he prefers going by train to using his car.

3 That dress is covered in diamonds. It .... cost her lots of money!

4 She .... made the dress herself. It's got a designer logo on it.

Is it worth it?

7 **a)** Phil and Dawn are planning a holiday together. Use the first Word Box to fill in the gaps in Phil's sentences with verb + *ing*. Use the second Word Box to complete Dawn's sentences with a noun.

visit	try	buy

let-down	money	tourist trap
energy	rip off	time

PHIL: Dawn, you've been there before. Do you think it's worth ....(1) things at the famous Tei-Kyo-Mu-Ni market?

DAWN: Not really. They only sell rubbish which you don't really need. It isn't worth the ....(2). And they try to overcharge you. It's a complete ....(3).

PHIL: How about the famous and beautiful Wai-Yu-Hia hill? Is it worth ....(4) to climb it?

DAWN: No, not really. It's very tiring, and when you get to the top, all you can see is a giant nuclear power station. It's a real ....(5). I don't think it's worth the ....(6), myself.

PHIL: OK then. Is it worth ....(7) Em-Ti Square? Sophie told me that it's really impressive to look at.

DAWN: No, let's not go there. The locals don't go near it at all. It's just a ....(8). And it takes ages to get there. It's simply not worth the ....(9).

PHIL: Er ... Dawn, why exactly *are* we going?

b) (53) Now listen and check.

c) Put these adjectives in pairs, and write them in two columns, one for extreme adjectives, and the other for less extreme adjectives.

terrific	tiring	big	beautiful	terrible
funny	hot ✓	pretty	good	hilarious
boiling ✓	bad	exhausting	enormous

Extreme	Less extreme
boiling	hot

d) Phil and Dawn are telling a friend about their holiday. Phil had a great time, but Dawn didn't really enjoy it. Use the words from Exercise 7c) to write Dawn's sentences.

PHIL: The weather! It was absolutely boiling!

DAWN: Oh, come on. It wasn't that hot.

PHIL: And I met this beautiful girl, Lai-Kyu.

DAWN: I don't think ....(1)!

PHIL: She had an enormous pair of eyes!

DAWN: They ....(2)! They were really piggy.

PHIL: You're just jealous. She had a great sense of humour. She was absolutely hilarious!

DAWN: Was she? I don't remember laughing. She ....(3).

PHIL: Anyway, I walked up Wai-Yu-Hia hill with her. It was exhausting!

DAWN: It can't have been ....(4). You seemed to have lots of energy later in the evening.

PHIL: Anyway, I had a terrific time.

DAWN: It ....(5). I've had better holidays.

PHIL: But Dawn was terrible company. She really got on my nerves.

DAWN: Was I? I don't think ....(6).

e) (54) Now listen and check.

Holiday in ruins

8 a) 🔘🔘 (55) **Listen to the first dialogue. A tour guide is showing some tourists around the ruins of Ancient Magnesia. Choose the correct answer.**

1 The man you hear talking is …
   a) a tour guide.
   b) a tourist.
   c) a local person.
2 The second woman who talks is …
   a) a tour guide.
   b) a tourist.
   c) a local person.
3 The guide thinks the place was used …
   a) for religious ceremonies.
   b) as a market place.
   c) as a place for sporting activities.
4 The man thinks the place was used …
   a) for religious ceremonies.
   b) as a market place.
   c) as a place for sporting activities.
5 The guide thinks the object was used …
   a) for combing women's hair.
   b) for making cows move faster.
   c) as a musical instrument.
6 The man thinks the object was used …
   a) for combing women's hair.
   b) for making cows move faster.
   c) as a musical instrument.

b) 🔘🔘 (56) **Listen to the second dialogue. Choose the correct answer.**

1 The man thinks that the tour was …
   a) good value for money.
   b) a complete rip-off.
   c) reasonably priced.
2 The woman thinks that the tour was …
   a) a waste of energy.
   b) a waste of time.
   c) a waste of money.
3 The woman thinks that the tour could have been …
   a) a let down.
   b) a once in a lifetime experience.
   c) better organised.
4 The woman thinks that her husband's behaviour …
   a) was extremely bad.
   b) was reasonable under the circumstances.
   c) was quite bad.
5 The man thinks his behaviour was …
   a) terrible.
   b) quite bad.
   c) not as bad as his wife thinks.

c) Rewrite these sentences using *must / might / can't have* + past participle.

1 I feel sure that the square was used for religious ceremonies.

....

2 It is possible that they kept animals there.

....

3 I feel sure that the square wasn't used for religious ceremonies.

....

4 Perhaps the people brought the animals through the arch.

....

5 It's possible that people came here to buy and sell animals.

....

6 I don't think she was trained very well for her job.

....

7 I feel sure that it was used for brushing women's hair.

....

8 It's impossible that it was used for brushing hair.

....

Do you remember? Units 10–12

The Passive

1 Rewrite these as passive sentences.
Leave out "*by* …" when you don't need to use it.

1 The Romans built this wall.

....

2 The police can arrest you for pretending to be a police officer.

....

3 Tadchester City won the football match.

....

4 Danny Beckenham scored the winning goal.

....

5 People are buying fewer computers these days.

....

6 At some point in the future, a large asteroid is going to hit the earth.

....

7 People send millions of e-mails every day.

....

8 Somebody should do something about it.

....

Reporting verbs

2 Decide which verb from the Word Box is associated with these sentences. Then use the verb to rewrite the sentence. Finally, change the sentence into Direct Speech.

(warn   promise   offer   refuse   apologise)

Example: She told him that she didn't want to marry him. _refuse_
She refused to marry him.
I don't want to marry you.

1 She said that she was sorry for arriving late. ....

....

....

2 He told her that he wouldn't forget to phone her mother. ....

....

....

3 He told her that another car was coming straight towards them. ....

....

....

4 She asked him if he wanted a cup of coffee.

....

....

....

5 The bank manager said that she couldn't lend him any more money. ....

....

....

6 He asked her if she wanted him to drive. ....

....

....

Deductions

3 a) Read this dialogue.

MAN: I'm certain it isn't modern. It's got an arm missing.
WOMAN: I'm sure it wasn't made like that.
MAN: Perhaps it's a representation of a powerless society.
WOMAN: Perhaps it fell off while they were bringing it to the museum.
MAN: Or maybe the artist knocked it off accidentally.
WOMAN: Yes. I'm sure he wasn't happy about that.
MAN: It's possible that he made it like that.
WOMAN: Perhaps it wasn't a man. Perhaps it was a woman.
MAN: That's a possible reason …
WOMAN: I'm sure another museum has the arm.

Rewrite the dialogue using *must / might / can't* and the correct tense.

MAN: It can't be modern. It's got an arm missing.

WOMAN: ....

MAN: ....

WOMAN: ....

MAN: ....

WOMAN: ....

MAN: ....

WOMAN: ....

b) 〇〇 (57) **Now listen and check.**

Do you remember everything?

1 a) Tick (✓) the correct sentences.

Example: Last year I've been to Morocco. ☐
Last year I went to Morocco. ✓
Last year I've gone to Morocco. ☐

1 (n) Have you been ever to China? ☐
(o) Did you go ever to China? ☐
(h) Have you ever been to China? ☐

2 (a) I met her while I was working in Spain. ☐
(t) I met her while I have worked in Spain. ☐
(h) I met her while I worked in Spain. ☐

3 (a) I've had by car since a long time. ☐
(v) I've had my car for a long time. ☐
(t) I've had my car for long time. ☐

4 (s) He not used to work in a hospital. ☐
(w) He didn't used to work in a hospital. ☐
(e) He didn't use to work in a hospital. ☐

5 (r) She often wears skirts, but today she
wears jeans. ☐
(y) She often wears skirts, but today she's
wearing jeans. ☐
(o) She often wear skirts, but today she
wearing jeans. ☐

6 (o) I think New York is a fantastic place! ☐
(n) I'm thinking New York is a fantastic place! ☐
(g) I'm think New York is a fantastic place! ☐

7 (y) She has ordered a burger when I was
seeing her. ☐
(u) She was ordering a burger when I saw her. ☐
(o) She has ordered a burger when I saw her. ☐

8 (u) My friend has moved to Tokyo, who is
called Nori. ☐
(s) Nori, who has moved, is my friend of Tokyo. ☐
(m) My friend, who is called Nori, has moved
to Tokyo. ☐

9 (a) If I go out, I'll buy some milk. ☐
(h) If I'll buy some milk, I go out. ☐
(o) If I will go out, I buy some milk. ☐

10 (u) Unless he loses that cough, he'll stop smoking. ☐
(l) Unless he stops smoking, he'll lose that cough. ☐
(d) Unless he stops smoking, he won't lose
that cough. ☐

11 (d) It's a really nice restaurant near my house. ☐
(e) There's a really nice restaurant near my house. ☐
(s) The restaurant near my house it's really nice. ☐

12 (d) She's excellent in speak English! ☐
(a) She's fantastic at speaking English! ☐
(o) Hers is English great! ☐

13 (s) Who did write the letter to the boss? ☐
(u) Who written the letter to the boss? ☐
(n) Who wrote the letter to the boss? ☐

14 (y) It's so enormous, I don't know what to
do with it. ☐
(m) It's such an enormous, I don't know what
to do with it. ☐
(g) It's such enormous, I don't know what to
do with it. ☐

15 (r) He's written a book and he's nearly finished it. ☐
(a) He's been writing a book and he's
nearly finishing it. ☐
(m) He's been writing a book and he's
nearly finished it. ☐

16 (m) If I didn't win the lottery, I would give all
my money away. ☐
(i) If I won the lottery, I wouldn't give any
of the money away. ☐
(a) If I would win the lottery, I would give
all the money away. ☐

17 (s) People meditate to relax. ☐
(r) People meditate for relax. ☐
(p) People meditate for relaxing. ☐

18 (r) My wife was leaving a note to say she went
away with the TV repair man. ☐
(t) My wife left a note to say she'd gone away
with the TV repair man. ☐
(k) My wife had left a note to say she was go
away with the TV repair man. ☐

19 (t) Someone had stolen everything because I
phoned the police. ☐
(a) Someone had stolen everything so I phoned
the police. ☐
(i) Someone had stolen everything so I phoning
the police. ☐

20 (s) She said me she would try coming to the party. ☐
(l) She told she was trying to come to the party. ☐
(k) She said she would try to come to the party. ☐

21 (l) Your friend said me he was trying to phone you. ☐
(e) Your friend told me he was trying to phone you. ☐
(u) Your friend told him you was trying
to phone you. ☐

22 (t) Don't forget to bring your coat otherwise
it'll rain. ☐
(s) Don't forget to bring your coat in case it rains. ☐
(z) Don't forget to bring your coat in case it
will rain. ☐

b) The letters you have ticked make a question.
Write them down here, then look through the test
to answer the question.

_ _ _ _ _ _ _ _ _ _ _ _ _ _ _ _ _ _ _ _ _?

If the answer is yes, then you should do something
about it!

Extend your reading Units 10–12

1 Read the article about a TV game show in Britain and answer the questions.

1 What is the game show called? ....
2 How long does it last? ....
3 How many people take part in it? ....

24-hour game show gives entrants no place to hide

Channel 4 revealed details yesterday of a game show in which ten contestants will be filmed every moment of the day and night as they attempt to live with each other for nine weeks.

Big Brother will allow viewers to follow almost every move that the volunteers make and to vote on which of them should be ejected from the contest each week, leaving the winner to collect a £70,000 prize.

The show, of which similar versions have proved hugely successful across Europe, will be transmitted twenty-four hours a day on the Internet and five nights a week on Channel 4.

The contestants, who were selected from 40,000 applicants, will live in a house built at a studio in east London. It will be surrounded by fences and there will be security guards with dogs. They will have access to an on-site psychotherapist for a one-hour session each week if the stress gets too much.

Producers said the series was a serious experiment in human interaction and not simply voyeuristic entertainment. Contestants had been chosen for their ability to get on with each other rather than argue, they said. The series editor said, "It would be unbearable in a programme like this for them to clash. If we put in nine people and a lunatic, it would be great television for a day and then they'd all want to leave."

Infra-red cameras will allow contestants to be filmed in the dark. Each will wear a radio mike which may be removed only in the shower and in bed. Sleeping accommodation is two five-bed rooms. Provisions will be limited to flour, potatoes, pasta, rice and restricted amounts of fish and meat. As the contestants are free to leave at any time, producers have got twenty reserves who can be called in.

---

2 Complete the sentences with the words from the Word Box.

> clash   contestant   eject
> volunteer   voyeuristic

1 A .... is a person who does something without being forced to.

2 A .... is a person who is taking part in a competition.

3 If something is ...., it shows us the private details of people's lives.

4 If you .... with somebody, you fight or argue with them.

5 When you .... someone, you make them leave.

3 Are these statements true (T) or false (F)? Write *T* or *F* in the boxes.

1 The public votes each week for the next person to leave the house. ☐

2 You can see more of the show on the Internet than on television. ☐

3 The contestants can go out to visit a psychotherapist while they're in the show. ☐

4 The producers have chosen people who will argue with each other because this makes good television. ☐

5 Contestants have to wait until they have a shower or get into bed before they can take off their microphones. ☐

6 The contestants cannot leave the show before they are voted out. ☐

4 Read the article and choose the best summary, a), b) or c).

   a) There are going to be two new versions of "Big Brother" in the UK.

   b) There are going to be two programmes using people ejected from "Big Brother."

   c) There are going to be two programmes based on the "Big Brother" style of filming.

TV rivals follow *Big Brother*

The rise of voyeur television continued yesterday when the BBC and Channel 5 disclosed that they are to make two new programmes based on Channel 4's *Big Brother* format.

The BBC is to remake *Living in the Past*, the popular documentary series from the seventies which gave people Iron Age tools, clothes and food to see whether they could make a settlement like their ancestors.

The new series, *Surviving the Iron Age*, will feature some of the children of those from the original show. Because it is a public service, the BBC will have to add an element of experimentation and education to the series.

By contrast, Channel 5 is blatantly imitating *Big Brother*. *Jailbreak*, which will begin in September, is so keen to cash in on *Big Brother's* popularity that it is considering using one of the show's ejectees.

"It is no secret that we tried to buy the rights to *Big Brother* and were beaten by Channel 4", Dawn Airey, programming director of Channel 5, said yesterday. "But now we have produced our most ambitious and expensive programme ever which combines two of television's current obsessions — reality television and big payout game shows."

In *Jailbreak* ten 'prisoners' chosen from the public will be housed in a specially built prison.

The contestants will follow a similar regime to real inmates, be surrounded by an 18ft fence and be guarded by thirty former prison officers. The studio/prison will be run by the former governor of Swansea prison, Jim Heyes. The first contestant or contestants to break out will win £100,000, with the prize money reducing by half for each of those who escapes afterwards.

The contestants will have to decide whether to cooperate in the escape and share the money or break out individually. There are escape routes built into the set and viewers can also win up to £10,000 by e-mailing or calling in with tips for the contestants.

5 Match the words (1–7) to their meanings (a–g).

A	B
1 format	a) prison
2 blatantly	b) a useful piece of advice
3 jail	c) escape
4 inmate	d) the arrangement of something
5 break out	e) the place where a TV programme is made
6 set	f) shamelessly
7 tip	g) someone who is kept in a prison or hospital

6 Read the article again and answer the questions.

1 What did people have to do in *Living in the Past*?

....

2 How is *Surviving the Iron Age* connected to *Living in the Past*?

....

3 Why does the BBC have to make *Surviving the Iron Age* educational?

....

4 Why does Channel 5 want to use someone from *Big Brother* in *Jailbreak*?

....

5 Who will the "prisoners" of *Jailbreak* be?

....

6 What is their task while they are in "prison"?

....

7 Who will get more money in *Jailbreak*: the first contestant to escape, or the last?

....

8 How can the contestants escape?

....

9 Who will get more money: someone who escapes alone, or someone who escapes with others?

....

10 How can viewers get involved in the programme?

....

Extend your grammar Units 10–12

1 Fill in each gap in the text with one word from the Word Box. There are some words you won't need.

although	asked	by	can	do	did	flight	get	had	however	involving
luckily	making	managed	must	so	taking	that	to	were	which	who

Aeroplane Etiquette

Along with other frequent fliers I have always complained that young children parents with children ruin flights. Children have tantrums, kick seats, make a mess with their food and generally misbehave. ....(1), some of the worst in-flight incidents I have seen were caused ....(2) business travellers ....(3) feel they deserve special treatment just because they fly ....(4) frequently.

Surprisingly, aeroplane etiquette violations ....(5) have serious consequences. You may have read about a recent case in the newspapers: a businessman and a female executive met on an American Airlines ....(6) from Dallas to London. They became drunk and ended up undressing in business class. ....(7) they were asked to behave by fellow passengers, flight attendants and the pilot, they persisted. The executives eventually lost their jobs, ...(8) fined heavily in British courts and became an inspiration for late-night television jokes.

As you can imagine, most problems occur in the cramped, overcrowded economy sections of aeroplanes and they usually centre around luggage, personal space and ....(9) noise. As an illustration, let me tell you about a recent incident ....(10) a businessman travelling next to me in the economy section of a plane.

The problems started when we boarded the plane. He was carrying an oversized bag over his shoulder and he ....(11) to hit the heads of every single passenger down one side of the aisle as he proceeded to his seat. ....(12), I was walking behind the man, so I didn't ....(13) hit. However, I'd soon suffer this man's lack of respect for others …

First of all, his bag was so big ....(14) it took up most of the space in the overhead locker. When I politely ....(15) him to put his bag under the seat in front of him, he simply told me ....(16) get a flight attendant to help me. By this time he had, of course, taken my seat because, as he said, he preferred to have the window seat. He also made sure he had both armrests to himself.

Unfortunately, his behaviour got worse during the course of the flight. He ....(17) have been very hungry because he took and ate my snack immediately after it was served. His only comment was: "You don't really want to eat this, ...(18) you?" Then he got ready for a little siesta by ....(19) off his shoes and reclining his seat all the way before the person behind him ....(20) finished eating. Wouldn't life be much easier if people like this gentleman were not allowed to use public transport?

Next time you travel by plane, please remember to be considerate. Etiquette rules also apply in the air!

2 Complete the second sentence so that it means the same as the first sentence.
Use the word in capitals in the second sentence.

1 The police arrested them for reckless driving.
GOT
They ....for reckless driving.

2 They gave him a ten-year sentence.
GIVEN
He .... a ten-year sentence.

3 They can't go out on Sundays.
ALLOWED
They .... go out on Sundays.

4 I finally managed to get tickets for the film you wanted.
SUCCEED
I finally .... tickets for the film you wanted.

5 Unfortunately, I didn't manage to get the seats you wanted.
ABLE
Unfortunately, I .... the seats you wanted.

6 He said he wouldn't help us.
REFUSED
He .... help us.

7 They said they would come to the theatre with us.
AGREED
They .... to the theatre with us.

8 I am sure he wasn't on that plane with you.
CAN'T
He .... been on that plane with you.

Extend your writing Units 10–12

1 The opinions of four different groups of people are given in the report: the government (G), the writer (W), people for censorship (F) and people against censorship (A). Read these opinions, check in the article who thinks this. Then write the letter **G, W, F** or **A** in the boxes.

There has always been violence in the world. ☐

More young people are violent now than before. ☐

Children have to learn other ways of solving their problems from their parents. ☐

It is better to understand violence than to ignore it. ☐

There is a link between watching violence on TV and an increase in aggression. ☐

It's not TV that makes you violent, some people are already like that. ☐

There are other things that children can do besides watching TV. ☐

2 Read the text again and complete the gaps with the words and expressions from the box below.

| As a result | Firstly | Finally | In contrast | moreover | not only (x 2) | but also (x 2) |
| on the other hand | | In my opinion | In addition | The purpose of this report | | and |

Censorship

The background to the report (1)

As a result of recent incidents of violence by young people, the government have asked the TV industry to cut down the amount of violence shown when young people are watching. This increase in censorship has started a discussion between those who think that it is necessary and those who, ...(1), think that it takes away people's freedoms.

The purpose of the report (2)

.................................(2) is to outline the arguments for and against censorship and to suggest some practical steps that can be taken.

Arguments for the censorship of TV violence (3)

.................................(3), it is necessary to say that the government's request is based on the idea that the media can have a bad effect on young people. And this would seem to be true. Hundreds of studies have shown that after watching a lot of violence, ...(4) do young people begin to see it as normal, ...(5) they accept violence as a way to solve their own problems. ....(6) they become more generally more aggressive.

Arguments against the censorship of TV violence (4)

.................................(7), many people think that those who copy violence already have a psychological problem. They say, ...(8), that the media simply reflect the ideas and feelings that are already in society ....(9) that there were many examples of violent behaviour in history long before the invention of television. ....(10) they argue that if children only see "good" events and actions, they will not learn to see both sides of different situations and make balanced decisions about them.

The writer's opinion (5)

.................................(11), whatever the government decision is, parents should take more responsibility in this. They should discuss the terrible effects of real violence with their children, show them that it is not the way to solve their problems and, ...(12), teach them ....(13) how to watch TV ....(14) how to turn it off!

3 Now write a short report of your own about the use of mobile phones. Follow the outline of the report above and use the ideas below.

Fact: Now increasing restrictions on the use of mobile phones: e.g. quiet carriages in trains, no use in golf clubs. Some like phones, some hate.

Purpose of report: to look at some advantages and disadvantages of mobile phones.

Advantages: useful to contact family and friends 24/7. in dangerous situations e.g. the car entertain and inform us e.g. games and Internet access

Disadvantages: possible health problems especially for the young.
annoy people in the same place and stop them talking to each other! Expensive. More theft, especially amongst young people

Personal opinion: use should be controlled in public places but not me first!

Answer Key

Unit 1 It takes all sorts

1

1 chatty   2 upset   3 stupid   4 nasty
5 friendly   6 weird   7 boring   8 intelligent

2

1 Both Sheila and Dave went to Australia in 1999.
2 Both Dave and Sheila have been to Poland.
3 Dave and Sheila went to Morocco in the same year.
4 Dave has been to Argentina and India.
5 Sheila has been to Russia, but she hasn't been to South Africa.
6 Sheila has been to Russia, but Dave hasn't.
7 Sheila went to India the year before Dave.

3

1 Has Dave ever been to Poland?
2 No, she hasn't.
3 Did Dave go to India in 1997?
4 No, they haven't.
5 Have Dave and Sheila both been to Argentina?
6 No, they didn't.

4a), b), c) and d) 🔊 (1)

1 Have you ever been to Poland?
  Yes, I have.
2 When did you go?
  Two years ago.
3 Have you travelled much?
  Yes, I have.
4 When did you go to Japan?
  About three months ago.
5 Where did you go on holiday?
  I went to Kenya.
6 When were you there?
  A year ago.

5a) 🔊 (2)

SHEILA: So there I was, in Morocco, and I decided to get the train from Tangier down to Rabat, the capital. There was an English guy on the train, too, who was travelling with a couple of friends.

DAVE: Yeah, go on …

s: Well, I was with my friend, Trudi, and she started talking to one of the guys, I forget his name now. He looked a bit like you, though! Perhaps a little taller. And his hair was different. Anyway, I didn't like him very much. He kept on talking about how many different places he'd been to.

D: Well, it takes all sorts, I suppose.

s: Anyway, the train stopped at a little station along the way, and the guys decided to go across to a little café we could see from the train. Just to get some soft drinks.

D: Yeah, go on …

s: So, anyway, we thought up a little plan. When the guys got back, we told them the name of a restaurant in Rabat, and we arranged to meet up there that night. The guys seemed really keen.

D: Go on …

s: Well, we just made the name up. It didn't exist at all! Let me remember, I think we called it …

SHEILA AND DAVE: "Le Mange Tout".

s: Oh my god! It wasn't …

D: Yes, it was me and my friends. We spent ages looking for that place.

s: Oh, no! I'm so sorry! It just seemed like a fun idea at the time.

D: Well, it wasn't such fun for us!

s: Listen … oh, how embarrassing! … what a small world! … I didn't know it was you. I shouldn't have told you the story. You seem such a nice guy.

D: Hey, don't worry. It was a long time ago. To tell you the truth, we didn't actually look for the restaurant anyway. We were all a bit tired, so we had an early night.

s: Oh, you pig! Hey, you look really different now.

D: Well, my hair is shorter … Say, have you ever been to South Africa?

1 = T   2 = T   3 = T   4 = T   5 = F   6 = F
7 = T   8 = T

5b)

1 met   2 friendly   3 have met   4 was
5 boring   6 made up   7 meet   8 upset
9 friendly   10 told   11 embarrassed
12 went   13 visited   14 ate   15 romantic

6a)

1 've known   2 for   3 've been   4 since
5 's been   6 for   7 got married   8 've loved
9 since   10 've had

6b)

1 've known   2 went   3 sang   4 fell
5 's had   6 since   7 loved   8 haven't loved
9 since   10 've tried   11 became
12 've been   13 for

c)

1 = T   2 = F   3 = T   4 = T   5 = F   6 = F

d) and e) 🔊 (3)

We had **nothing in common**, baby
But I could always **depend** on you
And though I've got **a life of my own**
I'm sad that I've lost you.
We didn't really **get on**, baby
Will my loneliness never end?
And now you've gone, I'm all **alone**
You ran away with **my best friend**.
I've loved you **since I met you**, baby
Though that was only **three hours** ago
You called me strange, desperate and **boring**
Well, now I'm miserable also.
I guess I'm just a **crazy**, mixed-up guy.

7

perfect man	Alvin
self-confident	insecure
hard-working	lazy
patient	impatient
generous	mean
outgoing	shy
sincere	two-faced
sensitive	insensitive
sociable	unsociable

8a)

1 used to/would go out   2 used to feel
3 used to/would sleep   4 used to do
5 used to have   6 used to/would buy
7 used to be

9a)

1 It's your first day on a new course. You go to the coffee bar, and there are lots of people chatting.
2 Which of these describes how you spend your free time?
3 You have been invited to a party, where there are lots of people who you've never met before.
4 Which of these describes you at work?
5 A friend has just split up with their partner.
6 You are waiting for a bus. It hasn't arrived after 15 minutes.

b)

1 self-confident a	not very confident b	balanced c
2 sociable b	unsociable c	balanced a
3 outgoing a	shy b	balanced c
4 hard-working b	lazy c	balanced a
5 sensitive b	insensitive a	balanced c
6 patient b	impatient c	balanced a

9c)

1 second   2 first   3 third

2 In the city

1a)

1 pavement   2 monument   3 lamp-post
4 balcony   5 railing   6 rooftop   7 building
8 road sign   9 post box   10 traffic light
11 phone box   12 skyscraper

2a) 🔊 (4)

TIM: Excuse me, could you tell me how to get to the Metro Hotel?

AMERICAN: Sure. You go past this store, as far as the parking lot.

T: Yes …

A: Then turn right, and walk past a large apartment block, which has a mailbox outside.

T: Yes …

A: Then you turn left, and cross the street to the opposite sidewalk.

T: Yes …

A: Keep going, past the subway entrance and you can't miss it.

T: Er … past the … er …

A: Or, you could just take a cab.

T: Sorry, could you tell me again?

1 store   2 parking lot
3 apartment block   4 mailbox
5 sidewalk   6 subway   7 cab

b) 🔊 (5)

I live in Croydon, South London. It isn't too far from the centre of the city, and also it's quite easy to get out into the countryside, too. Some people think it's really ugly, but I love living there! Shopping is easy … There's a big shopping centre, lots of little shops, and you can get everything you need. It's a very cosmopolitan place … people from a lot of different countries live there. There aren't many tourists, though. It isn't the sort of place people go to visit. There aren't really many tourist attractions, like monuments or statues. I suppose it looks quite dirty, sometimes … people drop a lot of litter on the streets, and a lot of rubbish gets left outside the shops and restaurants. There are lots of restaurants, and you can get food from many different countries. Some important roads pass through Croydon, and there's a lot of traffic, which means there's also a lot of pollution. Croydon has a lot of pubs and nightclubs, and so it can be quite noisy at night. There are lots of cinemas in Croydon, and plenty of parks quite nearby. You can easily get the train in to central London, and there is a wonderful tram system, too. Oh, and taxis … there are plenty of taxis!

1 = F   2 = F   3 = T   4 = T   5 = F
6 = F   7 = T   8 = T   9 = T   10 = F

3

1 There isn't much tourism.
2 There are a lot of cars.
3 There isn't much noise at night.
4 There's a lot of litter on the streets.
5 There aren't many nightclubs.
6 There are a lot of taxis.

4a)

1 … and ~~stay~~ *I'm staying* here in London
2 Normally ~~I'm taking~~ *I take* my car to work
3 ~~I'm having~~ *I have* a lot of friends
4 ~~I get to know~~ *I'm getting to know* lots of people

b)

live / Zurich = U, study / London = N, use / public transport = N, go out / a lot = N, eat / healthy food = U, put on / weight = N, meet / new friends = N, stay at home / evenings = U, drive / work = U, share a flat / other students = N, have / a lot of friends = U, live / parents = U, work / bank = U, study / language school = N

1 She usually works in a bank, but now she's studying at a language school.
2 She usually lives with her parents, but now she's sharing a flat with other students.
3 She normally drives to work, but now she's using public transport.
4 Most of the time she stays at home in the evenings, but now she's going out a lot.
5 She generally eats healthy food, but now she's putting on weight.

c)

1 Is she studying in Paris?
   No, she isn't. She's studying in London.
2 Does she usually live with her boyfriend?
   No, she doesn't. She lives with her parents.
3 Is she sharing a flat with other students?
   Yes, she is.
4 Does she usually take the bus to work?
   No, she doesn't.
5 Does she have a lot of friends in Zurich?
   Yes, she does.
6 Is she eating well at the moment?
   No, she isn't.

5a) and b) 🔊 (6)

1 [w] <u>Are</u> you studying English?
   Yes, I [s] <u>am</u>.
2 Anna [w] <u>has</u> a lot of friends in Zurich.
3 Where [w] <u>are</u> you going?
   To the airport. My parents [w] <u>are</u> coming to visit.
4 [w] <u>Have</u> you ever been to Washington?
   No, I [s] <u>haven't</u>.
5 What [w] <u>do</u> you [s] <u>do</u>?
6 [w] <u>Are</u> they coming to the party?
   Yes, they [s] <u>are</u>.

6

Incorrect sentences are: 2, 3, 5, 6, 7.
Corrections are:
1 I think it's a wonderful city.
2 I have a job in a burger bar.
3 I'm working with an Italian woman who comes from Bari.
4 She doesn't understand me when I speak English.
5 I think she likes me.

7

1 When I got to the airport, my parents were waiting for me.
2 I met my wife when I was working in a hospital. Now I work in a school.
3 I wanted to get a job in advertising, but I didn't have the right qualifications.
4 I saw a man standing on the corner. He was wearing a dark coat and a big hat.
5 The phone rang when I was having a bath.
6 I lost my wallet when I was shopping in Oxford Street.
7 I was waiting for the bus when I saw them.
8 What were you doing when you saw the man standing on the corner?

8

1 Is he?
2 I lived in Ireland when I was a boy.
3 Were you?
4 Is it?
5 Do I?
6 They usually drive to work.
7 Was he?
8 He was my best friend when I was a child.

9a) and b)

1 = F   2 = F   3 = T   4 = F   5 = T

c)

1 expatriate   2 fictional   3 district
4 flyover   5 omnibus

d)

1 manages   2 gets   3 has had
4 have   5 used to live   6 has been

10a) 🔊 (7)

I was sitting in a bar in New Orleans, when she walked in. She was wearing a summer dress, although it was raining outside. She ordered a dry Martini and then sat down at my table. She blew smoke in my face, and said, "What's a nice guy like you doing in a place like this?"

I told her she had beautiful eyes. She must have put something in my drink, because the next morning I woke up in a strange room. There was a lot of noise from a band playing jazz in the street outside, and there was a strange smell. I looked around, and I noticed that a cigarette was burning in the ashtray. Suddenly I noticed that a woman was standing in the doorway. It was the woman who was in the bar the night before. She turned and ran out. I followed her. When I got out into the street, it was hot, the sun was shining, and the band was still playing. I couldn't see her anywhere.
Summary 2 is correct.

b)

1 Johnny was sitting in a bar.
2 The woman came into the bar.
3 She ordered a dry Martini.
4 Johnny told her she had beautiful eyes.

5 The woman put something in Johnny's drink.

6 Johnny woke up in a strange room.

7 Johnny saw the woman. She was standing in the doorway.

8 Johnny followed the woman into the street.

9 Johnny couldn't see the woman.

c)

1 was having a drink, walked

2 was wearing, was raining

3 asked for

4 thought

5 didn't know

6 woke up, was playing

d)

1 there was   2 There were   3 they were

4 There was   5 it was

e) and f) 👀 (8)

I walked along the street. It was Mardi Gras, and a lot of people *were dancing* [(1)] and singing. I saw a police officer, and I asked him where I was. He laughed, and said "You're in Basin Street. And you should go easy on the beer. It's only noon." I kept on walking, but I felt nervous. I was sure that someone *was following* [(2)] me. I turned around suddenly. Two men *were standing* [(3)] right behind me. They got out a map, and looked at it. I went over to them and asked them how to get to Jackson Square. They pretended not to understand me, and answered me in bad English. I kept on walking. When I turned around again, they were still behind me, but they *were looking* [(4)] at a poster on a wall. I continued walking. Then I saw the woman again. She was standing against a wall. She *was smoking* [(5)] a cigarette. When she saw me, she *disappeared* [(6)] round a corner. I ran after her. Suddenly, from nowhere, someone shouted "Hey, Johnny … Johnny Damone". When I turned, someone *hit* [(7)] me over the head with the lid of a trashcan … I realised then that I had to leave town.

3 When Saturday comes

1

1		S	W	E	A	T	Y		
2	F	R	I	E	N	D	L	Y	
3		R	E	L	A	X	E	D	
4				C	O	S	Y		
5			N	O	I	S	Y		
6			S	M	O	K	Y		
7		S	P	A	C	I	O	U	S
8	F	A	S	H	I	O	N	A	B	L	E
9			B	R	I	G	H	T		

2a) and b)

1 He's the man who / that asked me if I wanted to dance. ✓

2 We're meeting at the restaurant where we ate last week.

3 I heard the song (which / that) you like. ✓✗

4 There's a man over there who / that looks like your brother. ✓

5 Is she the woman whose daughter lives in your street?

3

1 Derek, who asked me if I wanted to dance, is very handsome.

2 The restaurant, which serves wonderful English food, is closed on Sundays.

3 The song, which is by the group "Six Pack", is at the top of the charts.

4 My friend, who was in the film *Pass the Salt*, is an actor.

5 The house, where I was born, is in Hill End Lane.

4a)

go out (1)

spend all my money (2)

not be able to get taxi home (3)

have to walk (4)

get home late (5)

1 If I go out, I'll spend all my money.

2 If I spend all my money, I won't be able to get a taxi home.

3 If I can't get a taxi home, I'll have to walk.

4 If I have to walk, I'll get home late.

b)

1 b) Unless I save up my money, I won't have enough for a holiday.

2 e) Unless I apologise, she won't talk to me again.

3 a) Unless you stop smoking, you won't get rid of that cough.

4 c) Unless you stop eating cakes, you'll put on weight.

5 d) Unless you stop doing that, I'll get angry.

5

1 'm going to / unless / will

2 'm going to / if / 'll / 'm going to

3 'm going to / If / won't / 'm going to / If / won't

6a) and b) 👀 (9)

1 A: That film was very good.
  B: Good? It was absolutely brilliant!

2 A: That show was very funny.
  B: Funny? It was absolutely hilarious!

3 A: This burger's big.
  B: Big? It's absolutely enormous!

4 A: This chicken's very nice.
  B: Nice? It's absolutely delicious!

5 A: The coffee tastes awful.
  B: Awful? It's absolutely disgusting!

6 A: I'm feeling hungry. How about you?
  B: Hungry? I'm absolutely starving!

7a)

1 a prediction   2 a warning

3 a promise   4 a threat

b)

1 If I marry him, the marriage won't last.

2 If I don't find a proper job, I won't be successful.

3 If she marries me, I'll make her a rich woman.

4 If he doesn't marry me, he'll never see me again.

c)

a) 3   b) 4   c) 1   d) 2

1 love   2 be sad   3 know   4 try

5 resent it and leave you   6 let him go

7 be honest   8 all end in tears

9 miss a wonderful opportunity

10 what you want to do

8a) and b) 👀 (10)

1 The all-new, ten-screen CineFactory. The latest Hollywood blockbusters. Family films, late-night shows, classic movies, and … our Saturday morning children's cinema club. For the best in on-screen entertainment, come to the CineFactory.

2 Going out tonight? Want to go clubbing? Fancy something different? Then come to the Club Tropicana, for a great evening. Fantastic music, wonderful atmosphere, the best DJs in town. Over 18s only. Club Tropicana. Drinks are free before 10 p.m.!

3 The recently refurbished Emilia Centre is proud to present a new comedy by English writer Ray Buckling, called *Pasta Disaster*. Three suburban couples have a dinner party. All seems well until Annabel tells them what's in her secret recipe! *Pasta Disaster*. The critics called it "a hilarious adult comedy"! At the Emilia Centre.

4 Have we got a good deal for you! All you can eat for the price of a single meal! And a beer, or a glass of Italian wine … on the house! Fridays, from 6–7 p.m. at Luigi's. Delicious, fresh food, made to Mamma's secret recipe. Bring the children too! There's a great family atmosphere.

5 Come to O'Connor's, for a great evening out. Traditional Irish beer, mouth-watering Irish food, wonderful Irish hospitality. O'Connor's. An Irish pub that's not just for Irish people. We also have a fabulous garden at the back, so children are welcome at lunchtimes, too.

CineFactory is a cinema.

Luigi's is a restaurant.

Club Tropicana is a nightclub.

Emilia Centre is a theatre.

O'Connor's is a pub.

CineFactory, Luigi's, and O'Connor's are good for families.

b)

1 Family films ✔
Saturday morning children's cinema club ✔
Ten screens ✔
Classic movies ✔
Late-night shows ✔
The latest Hollywood blockbusters ✔
2 Fantastic.
3 Wonderful
4 Nothing
5 Because drinks are free before 10 p.m.
6 *Pasta Disaster*
7 False
8 All you can eat for the price of one meal.
9 False
10 False

c)

1 good   2 meal   3 dishes   4 waiters
5 family   6 excellent   7 busy   8 feel
9 having   10 delicious   11 want
12 to have   13 will like

d) 👓 (11)

The play was described on the radio advert as "a hilarious adult comedy", but I didn't think it was funny at all! The acting was absolutely awful, and the only funny part was when the character Annabel fell off the stage! The theatre itself was absolutely freezing, it was also filthy, and the seats are really tiny. And there was a woman in front of me with an enormous hat, so I couldn't see anything anyway! Unless you give me my money back, I'll write to the management.

1 The woman didn't like the theatre or the play.
2 it wasn't funny ✔
the acting was bad ✔
the theatre was cold ✔
the theatre was dirty ✔
the seats were small ✔
she couldn't see ✔

9a)

1 feel like doing   2 should go
3 Let's eat out   4 don't want to go
5 'd like to have   6 Why don't we do

b) 👓 (12)

ANN: Do you like going to pubs, or do you prefer nightclubs?

BRENDAN: Well, I suppose pubs, really, given the choice.

A: Really? Why's that, then?

B: Well, firstly I don't like dancing that much. And secondly, I don't like the music you get in clubs these days. It's just so boom … boom … boom … repetitive … no tune. How about you?

A: Oh, clubs, definitely. I enjoy listening to the music, and I love dancing. I don't

enjoy sitting in a pub all evening, drinking lots of beer.

B: Well, you don't have to drink beer…

A: Yeah, I suppose so. What about when the pub closes? What do you do then?

B: Sometimes I feel like going home and watching a good video. But my favourite thing is going for a curry after the pub. A really nice meal to finish off the evening. Then home to watch a video.

A: Yeah, I like a curry from time to time, too.

B: What about you, after you've been to the club?

A: Well, it's usually quite late, or should I say quite early in the morning, so sometimes I go back to a friend's house, or just go home. But what I really love doing is going to an Internet café, to check my e-mails, or just surf the Web. Then I like going back to a friend's house, for a big breakfast.

B: Yeah, those cafés are quite cool. I've been to them a few times.

going to clubs A
going for a curry A and B
going to an Internet café A and B
dancing A
going home to watch a video B
listening to music A
going to a friend's house A
going to pubs B

c) and d) 👓 (13)

A: There's a really good bar near here.

B: Really? What's it like?

A: The atmosphere's really calm and relaxed, and it doesn't get too crowded. It's very spacious, and you can always find somewhere to sit.

B: What sort of people go there?

A: You get all sorts of different nationalities. It's very cosmopolitan.

B: What's it like inside?

A: It's comfortable and cosy. You can sit and read the newspaper. They serve food, too. I had a really delicious meal there once.

B: What sort of music do they play?

A: Oh, there isn't any music. It isn't a noisy place. It's open until midnight. Do you want to go? Come on! Everyone goes there! It's very fashionable!

B: No. It doesn't sound like my kind of place.

1 relaxed   2 crowded   3 spacious
4 cosmopolitan   5 cosy   6 delicious
7 noisy   8 fashionable

10

1 I'm giving a presentation at work.
2 I'm doing my washing.

3 I'm having dinner with Chastity.
4 I'm going to the theatre with my parents.
5 I'm playing golf with Tom.

11a)

1 The Hard Rock Café   2 Sarastro
3 Babe Ruth's   4 La Pergola

b)

1 c   2 c   3 b   4 b   5 a

Do you remember? Units 1–3

1a)

1 Have you ever been to Paris? f)
2 Did you go there on holiday? c)
3 What did you do there? e)
4 When did you go there? d)
5 Did you visit any famous monuments? b)
6 Who did you go with? a)

b)

1 went   2 was   3 was   4 did
5 learned   6 got   7 felt   8 went
9 became   10 've been   11 was
12 decided   13 had to   14 was
15 took   16 enjoyed   17 've done

c)

1 When did you go parachuting? e)
2 Where did you go to do it? f)
3 How did you feel? a)
4 Who did you do it with? b)
5 Why did you do it? c)
6 How long did it take to come down? d)

2

1 is / 's   2 isn't   3 is / 's
4 is / 's doing   5 is swimming
6 to speak   7 will / 'll get
8 help   9 don't apologise   10 won't pay

Extend your reading Units 1–3

1

1 You begin to lose control of your life.
2 When you want to.
3 When you really want to say no (and it is in your best interest to say no).

2

a) 3   b) 1   c) 4   d) 2

3

a) 3   b) 4

4

1 lose your temper   2 end up
3 stand up for   4 builds up   5 stems from

5

a) 2   b) 3   c) 1   d) 4

6

1 F   2 T   3 T   4 T   5 F

7

1 b)   2 e)   3 d)   4 a)   5 c)

Extend your grammar Units 1–3

1

1 among   2 to   3 But   4 mix   5 their
6 It   7 compares   8 like   9 purpose
10 atmosphere   11 also   12 usage
13 only   14 this   15 than   16 those
17 However   18 its   19 with   20 certain

2

1 I would go out
2 was a lot of traffic
3 you don't leave at once,
4 opened three months ago
5 How about coming to stay
6 longer works as a
7 while (I was) on
8 has become more

Extend your writing Units 1–3

1

<u>Thanks</u> for the invitation to your wedding <u>Great</u> to hear that <u>you and Tom</u> are getting married <u>at last!</u> <u>Sorry</u> that I <u>haven't been in touch</u> sooner to <u>tell</u> you that <u>I'm sorry that</u> I <u>won't be able to make it cos'</u> I've been having <u>a few</u> problems with <u>the flat where I live.</u> I <u>feel as though I've got to</u> move house. It's very time-consuming trying to <u>sort it all out.</u> The <u>thing</u> is that <u>I've never got on</u> with my flatmates. We <u>haven't got very much</u> in common and they're <u>really</u> untidy. Also there is <u>one weird guy</u> called Liam who <u>hasn't got a job.</u> <u>The other day</u> I saw him taking some <u>that I thought was</u> mine from the <u>fridge.</u> I was so tired after a <u>bad</u> day at work that I <u>shouted at him for</u> <u>nicking</u> it. It <u>turned out</u> it was his own food and now I think <u>I can't</u> <u>stay</u> there.
<u>A friend of a friend</u> has offered me a place <u>on her floor</u> for <u>a few days</u> but <u>I've got to</u> sort things out <u>a.s.a.p.</u> So that's why <u>I can't</u> come to the wedding.
<u>Get in touch</u> <u>when you get back</u> from your honeymoon and we can <u>fix a time</u> to <u>get together.</u> <u>I can't wait to see</u> your <u>photos!</u> <u>Sorry again.</u>
Take care and <u>write soon.</u>
<u>All the best to you both.</u>
Emma.

2

Dear Ms Swinburne
I was very pleased to receive your e-mail informing me that you have arranged an appointment to view a flat. I apologise that I have not written sooner. I was not able to do so due to the fact that I have only recently returned from a business trip.
I am afraid, however, that I am unable to attend the appointment on Thursday due to problems with my car.

A friend is able to drive me there on Wednesday. Would it be possible to reschedule the appointment for that day? I hope this is acceptable as I would like to move into a new flat as soon as possible.
I look forward to hearing from you at your earliest convenience. Apologies once again that I cannot attend the appointment.
Yours sincerely,
Emma Hart

4 How do you do that?

1a)

1 Arthur   2 Glenda   3 Martha   4 Glen

b)

1 c)   2 d)   3 g)   4 e)   5 f)   6 h)
7 a)   8 b)

c)

1 Martha is extremely good at English.
2 Glen is quite good at Science.
3 Glenda is hopeless at sports.
4 Arthur is quite good at English.
5 Martha is not very good at Science.
6 Glen is extremely good at French.
7 Glenda is not very good at English.

2a)

1 a) German Shepherd   2 e) St Bernard
3 d) Great Dane   4 c) Golden Retriever
5 b) Poodle

b)

a) domesticated
b) characteristics, qualities
c) tasks   d) breeds   e) docile
f) huge, enormous   g) fetch   h) hunting
i) terrific, excellent   j) fur

c)

1 = a) and c)   2 = b) and c)
3 = a) and b)   4 = a) and c)
5 = a) and b)   6 = b) and c)

3a) 🎧 (14)

When I was young, I didn't really like school that much, and so I didn't do very well. There were lots of things that I was good at, but I didn't try very hard. I left school when I was fourteen, and I went to work. But before then I did learn to swim, and I did learn to ride a bicycle. I learned to swim first, because we lived quite near the sea, and I was very good at it. I wasn't so good at riding a bicycle, but once I learned, I loved it! When I left school, I started work in a hotel, as a waitress. But quite soon, I got a job in the kitchen, helping the chef, and it was there that I learned to cook. People tell me I'm very good at cooking, I really enjoy it.
Then I got married, to Arnold, and we had our children. Four of them, in all. After they'd all grown up and left home, I got

interested in learning things again. I went to night school, and I started learning French. I was forty-seven when I started. Arnold thought I was mad, because people like us didn't learn languages at all. But I really wanted to do it, and I found I was quite good at it. I carried on learning French for five years, until I had quite a good level. It was then that we started taking our holidays in France, because we had a bit more money without the children at home.
After I started learning French, I got interested in driving. Everyone told me I was a bit old to start, but I really wanted to. I found it hard at first, and I wasn't really that good at it. But in the end I passed my test, and I'm actually very good at it now. And recently, I've been learning to fly. My daughter bought me some lessons after Arnold died; she thought it would keep me occupied. I liked it so much that I carried on taking the lessons, and I've just got my pilot's licence. Not bad at sixty-five, eh? I love learning new things. Who said that you can't teach an old dog new tricks? The next thing I want to do is learn to play the piano … I'd love to be able to do that …

1 = F   2 = T

b)

1 swim   2 ride a bicycle   3 cook
4 speak French   5 drive
6 fly an aeroplane

c)

1 = T   2 = F   3 = F   4 = T   5 = F   6 = T
7 = F   8 = F   9 = F   10 = T   11 = T

4a)

1 g   2 d   3 e   4 f   5 c
6 i   7 a   8 b   9 j   10 h

b)

1 a   2 a   3 b, c   4 c   5 b
6 b, c   7 b   8 c   9 a, c   10 b, c

5a)

1 working   2 to work   3 dealing
4 persuading   5 work   6 meeting
7 selling   8 being   9 making
10 Having   11 managing
12 communicating   13 to hearing

b) 🎧 (15)

INTERVIEWER: Why exactly do you want to apply for the job, Mr Dyer?
GARY: Well, I think I'd be quite good at selling your products.
I: OK. How good are you at working under pressure?
G: Extremely good! After all, I managed to get my degree.
I: Lots of people do. I need to make sure that you actually want to work under

pressure. And I need you to persuade me that you are the best person for the job.

G: Er ... I'm extremely good at ... at ... er ... persuading people, and I'm not bad at making decisions. I think.

I: Are you any good at dealing with people? Look at me when I'm talking to you!

G: I think so. My mother thinks I am.

I: Well you haven't managed to persuade me, I'm afraid! Goodbye!!

G: I'm not bad at swimming.

1 to apply   2 selling   3 working
4 to get   5 to work   6 to persuade
7 persuading   8 making   9 dealing
10 to persuade   11 swimming

6a)
1 I could swim very well when I was a child.
2 Climbing the mountain was hard, but in the end we succeeded in reaching the top.
3 I'm not very good at languages, but I managed to pass my German exam.
4 The meeting was cancelled, so I was able to have a long lunch break.

b)
1 managed to   2 was able to
3 could   4 succeeded in

7a)
1 celebrated his 17th birthday
2 joined Everton
3 got married
4 played in the World Cup
5 got badly injured
6 retired

b)
1 = b)   2 = b)   3 = a)   4 = b)
5 = a)   6 = b)   7 = b)

c)
1 could   2 managed to   3 could
4 could   5 couldn't   6 wasn't able
7 succeeded in   8 couldn't

5 Culture vultures

1a)
a play = c)
a film = a)
an art gallery = d)
a photography exhibition = b)

b)
1 Poster c)
1 playwright   2 performances
3 play   4 audience
2 Poster d)
1 exhibition   2 paintings
3 artists   4 sculpture
5 installation
3 Poster b)
1 photographs   2 videos
3 computers   4 exhibits   5 website
4 Poster a)

1 film   2 director   3 performances
4 actors   5 box office

2a)

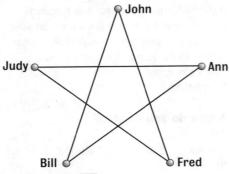

b), c) and d) 🔊 (16)
1 Who gave it to Fred? 0 John did.
2 Who did Bill give it to? S John.
3 Who gave it to John? 0 Bill did.
4 Who did Judy give it to? S Ann.
5 Who gave it to Ann? 0 Judy did.
6 Who did Fred give it to? S Judy.
7 Why did John give it to Fred? 0 He thought he might like it.
8 Why did Ann give it to Bill? 0 Because she forgot to buy him a present.

e) and f) 🔊 (16)
1 **Who** gave it to **Fred**?
2 **Who** did **Bill** give it to?
3 **Who** gave it to **John**?
4 **Who** did **Judy** give it to?
5 **Who** gave it to **Ann**?
6 **Who** did **Fred** give it to?
7 **Why** did **John** give it to **Fred**?
8 **Why** did **Ann** give it to **Bill**?

3a) and b) 🔊 (17)
VINCENT: So, Eric, are you going to tell me where you got your umbrella from?
ERIC: Well, Vincent, it was a gift from Godfrey himself.
V: From Godfrey? That is very unusual. Godfrey doesn't often give presents!
E: Well, when I say I got it from Godfrey, I don't mean that he gave it to me himself. No, it was more complicated than that.
V: Tell me more ...
E: Godfrey, I believe, gave it first to Jim. Jim used it for a while, then passed it on to Sam.
V: So, Jim got it from Godfrey, and gave it to Sam?
E: That is correct, Vincent.
V: And then did Sam give it to you?
E: No, it is more complicated still, my friend. Arnold, my dear friend Arnold, got it from Sam, who didn't like the colour. Then Arnold decided he didn't like the colour either, and so he gave it to me. So when I say that I got it from Godfrey, I

don't mean that I got it directly from him ... just in a roundabout way.
V: But where did Godfrey get it?
E: I gave it to him!
V: You gave it to him! You're telling me, Eric, that you gave it to Godfrey?
E: That is true, Vincent, my friend.
1 = T   2 = F

b)
1 f)   2 e)   3 b)
4 d)   5 a) / c)   6 a) / c)
1 Godfrey didn't give it directly to Eric.
2 Godfrey gave it to Jim.
3 Sam got it from Jim.
4 Sam gave it to Arnold, because he didn't like the colour.
5 Arnold didn't like the colour either, and so he gave it to Eric.
6 Eric gave it to Godfrey.

4a)
1 more unusual   2 more intelligent
3 more difficult   4 faster
5 more insecure   6 dangerous
7 bad   8 worse
9 easier   10 more beautiful
11 more creative   12 successful
13 comfortable

b)
1 Albert is slightly / a bit better at acting than Trevor.
2 Albert is slightly / a bit more intelligent than Trevor.
3 Albert is slightly / a bit more important than Trevor.
4 Trevor is far / a lot less handsome than Albert.

c) and d) 🔊 (18)
And so let's now turn to the other major film of this year, *Pass the Salt*, which also, of course, stars Celia Farmer, one of the co-stars of *Bus Driver*. And it would be very difficult indeed to find two more different films. Different in many aspects, but not so different in their financial success. *Bus Driver* has earned slightly more money, but *Pass the Salt* has also been financially successful. And I think for actor Trevor Smith, this has been more successful than his previous work, *Two Paintings*. This is a better film by far. He, of course, plays the character John, who is far less clever, far less intelligent than his wife, Jane, and she wins all their intellectual arguments. It is this intellectual side of *Pass the Salt*, where the main action takes place over the dinner table, that makes it a lot less exciting than *Bus Driver*. It is also more difficult to follow, too, to understand the ways in which the characters are thinking. *Bus Driver* is much easier to follow ...

d)
a) = T b) = T c) = F d) = T
e) = F f) = F g) = F
5
1 He's a film director. He's been making a film.
2 He's a poet. He's been writing a poem.
3 She's a presenter. She's been reading the news.
4 She's an artist. She's been painting a picture.
5 He's a photographer. He's been taking a picture.
6 She's a musician. She's been giving a concert.
7 He's a sculptor. He's been making a sculpture.
6
1 haven't seen   2 have you been doing
3 've been writing   4 have (you) completed
5 have written   6 have (you) been doing
7 have been having   8 have had
9 have set up   10 have made
7
1 looks like   2 might be   3 sort of
4 It looks as if   5 I suppose it's
8a) and b) 🔊 (19)
MARY: Hey, Jo, what's the matter? Why are your eyes all red? Have you been crying?
JO: Hi there, Mary. I've been watching a video. It was a really beautiful film.
M: What was it?
J: It's called *The Colour of Paradise*. It's an Iranian film.
M: Oh yeah, what's it about?
J: Well, it's about a boy, Mohammed, and he's blind.
M: Go on …
J: He goes to a boarding school in Tehran, the capital. It's a boarding school for blind children. He's been living in the countryside with his father, since his mother died … Anyway, his father has been finding it difficult to look after him, and has also been thinking about getting married again. So, he wants him to stay at the school.
M: What, Mohammed wants to stay at the school?
J: No, his father wants him to stay there. Mohammed wants to go home, to be with his sisters, and his grandmother, who he absolutely adores.
M: Aaaah …
J: Anyway, there's one scene, very near the beginning of the film, with no words at all. It's so moving. It's the last day of term, and all the children are waiting for their parents to arrive, and take them home. When we see Mohammed, he's

been sitting in the school garden, waiting and waiting. But his father doesn't arrive.
M: Aaah, poor thing.
J: Shhh, let me carry on!
M: Sorry …
J: He just looks so lonely, sitting there with this big pair of sunglasses on.
M: Sunglasses?
J: Well, he's blind.
M: Oh yeah, sorry …
J: Anyway, that means his hearing is really … really … you know … extremely good.
M: Uh-huh.
J: So, he's sitting there in the garden, and he hears this cat, walking around in the bushes. We can see it, of course, but he can't.
M: Yeah.
J: So, we watch it for a while, and you think it's going to go up to Mohammed and try to make friends with him.
M: Yeah.
J: But suddenly he starts throwing stones at it, to frighten it away.
M: Why's that?
J: Remember that he can hear really well. Well, he's heard a baby bird, which has fallen out of a tree, and he knows that the cat is going to kill it, and eat it. So the cat looks at him and runs off. Then we watch Mohammed find the bird, pick it up, climb the tree, slowly, and put the bird back in its nest.
M: And is it just a scene, or is it … you know, a metaphor for something?
J: Yeah, it's a metaphor. The bird is Mohammed, and the nest is home. The cat is the world he feels frightened of.
M: And what happens?
J: Well, his father takes him home in the end, though he doesn't want to, but sends him to work with a carpenter, who's also blind. I won't tell you the end, because you might want to watch it yourself, but anyway, it really is a beautiful film.
1 = F   2 = T   3 = F   4 = T   5 = T
b)
1 = T   2 = F   3 = T   4 = F   5 = T
6 = F   7 = T   8 = T
c)
1 has been looking   2 has been staying
3 wants   4 would like
5 has been sitting   6 has been waiting
7 has heard   8 has fallen
9 hears   10 throws
11 finds   12 wants

d)
1 Who, c)   2 Where, f)
3 Where, a)   4 What, b)
5 Where, d)   6 Who, e)
e)
1 so   2 such   3 so   4 such
5 such   6 so

6 Skin deep
1a)

Fiona	Arsenio
1 flared jeans	9 T-shirt
2 blouse	10 zip
3 pockets	11 patterned
4 pockets	12 jacket
5 buttons	13 tight trousers
6 belt-buckle	14 trainers
7 boots	
8 leather jacket	

2a) and b) 🔊 (20)
short-sleeved   sleeveless   mini
patterned   jacket   jumper
T-shirt   trousers   sweatshirt
c) and d) 🔊 (21)
high heels   sleeveless jumper   flared trousers   patterned sweatshirt
mini skirt   plain dress   striped top
tight blouse   checked shirt
e)
second   mini skirt
3a) and b) 🔊 (22)
In 1975, when I was about fourteen, I went to my first school disco. The other day, I found an old photo of myself, which my sister took before I went out. It's awful! My hair is really long and curly (now I wear it short), and the clothes are so horrible that I'm surprised my parents didn't make me stay at home. But they actually drove me to the disco! I was wearing a brown shirt with a huge collar, and a white sleeveless jumper with a big green stripe across the front. I also had dark green flared trousers, a belt with an enormous buckle and big platform shoes. I thought I looked really cool and stylish at the time, but now it seems like a fashion nightmare!
1 a)   2 b)   3 b)   4 b)   5 a)
b)
platform shoes ✓
brown shirt ✓
huge collar ✓
green stripe ✓
flared trousers ✓
enormous buckle ✓
white sleeveless jumper ✓
4a)
a) 'Shine-tastic!' toothpaste
b) 'Smooth-O' anti-wrinkle cream
c) 'Hair Today' anti-baldness cream
d) 'Beard-B-Gone' facial hair remover for men

b)

a) 1 the whitest / the brightest
2 the brightest / the whitest
3 the smelliest
4 the freshest

b) 1 The best
2 the cheapest
3 the quickest
4 the oldest
5 the youngest
6 most attractive

c) 1 the safest
2 the smoothest
3 the hairiest
4 oldest
5 the longest / the thickest
6 thickest / longest

d) 1 The cheapest
2 the quickest
3 the hairiest
4 the smoothest
5 the most effective

5a) and b) 👁👁 (23)

Hi, listeners, I'm Albert Dinero. Let me tell you about my life. I was born in New York, and I've lived there all my life. My family was poor. We never had much money, and I left school at fourteen to start work. I did lots of different jobs, and eventually I ended up as a bus driver. I did that for about five years before I became an actor. I worked mostly in the theatre at first, then I got some TV work, and finally I ended up in the movies. My first big film was called "Hot City Nights", and that's the one that made me famous. But now I find that I'm just not happy with my life. I want to change things, to get back to reality, back to normality. For a start, I have no privacy, my life is not my own. Everywhere I go, the press follow me. I don't like going out to restaurants any more. If it isn't the press, it's members of the public. Everywhere I go, it's "Hey, Albert, can I have your autograph?" or "Hey, Albert, can I take your photograph?" I'd like to be able to … you know … just do what I want, without people bothering me all the time. OK, so I'm rich, I'm famous, I have an apartment in New York and a house in California, I could, if I wanted to, buy expensive clothes and good food. But I don't. I don't enjoy it. I eat ordinary food, and wear cheap clothes. I appreciate what I have, but I'm still not happy, I still want to change things. I started thinking about it when I made my most recent film, "Bus Driver". There I was, I'd been a bus driver, and now I was a bus driver all over again! As I said to my therapist … I said that if I wasn't rich and famous, I wouldn't spend so much time in

therapy! I've thought about having plastic surgery. Not to improve my appearance, because, well, hey, I'm pretty good-looking, but I just think that if people didn't recognise me, I would be able to live a normal life. I want to be a bus driver again!

1 film star   2 rich   3 famous   4 unhappy
5 wants (to change his life)

b)

1 doesn't have   2 doesn't enjoy
3 doesn't like   4 can't
5 buys   6 wants
7 spends   8 hasn't had
9 become a bus driver

c), d) and e) 👁👁 (24)

1 If I wasn't a <u>film</u> star, I might be <u>happy</u>.
2 If I was <u>happy</u>, I wouldn't want to change my <u>life</u>.
3 If people didn't <u>follow</u> me, I might enjoy going to <u>restaurants</u>.
4 If my life was <u>different</u>, I could do what I <u>wanted</u>.
5 If I bought expensive clothes and <u>food</u>, I wouldn't enjoy them.
6 If I had a <u>simple</u> life, I might be <u>happier</u>.
7 If I was <u>happy</u>, I might not spend a lot of time in <u>therapy</u>.
8 If I had plastic <u>surgery</u>, people wouldn't <u>recognise</u> me.

6

1 He wishes he could change his life.
2 He wishes people didn't follow him everywhere.
3 He wishes he could enjoy going to restaurants.
4 He wishes he could do what he wants.
5 He wishes he had a simple life.
6 He wishes he didn't spent a lot of time in therapy.
7 He wishes people didn't recognise him.

7

1 forehead   2 chest   3 elbow
4 waist   5 wrist   6 thumb
7 finger   8 hip   9 thigh
10 knee   11 calf   12 toe
13 heel   14 ankle   15 eyebrows
16 eyelashes   17 cheek   18 ear
19 chin   20 neck   21 shoulder

8a)

1 do yoga: Picture 3
2 do weights: Picture 5
3 have a tattoo: Picture 6
4 lie on a sunbed: Picture 1
5 go jogging: Picture 4
6 go on a diet: Picture 2

b)

1 People do yoga to concentrate the mind.
2 People do weights to get bigger muscles.
3 People have tattoos to make a personal

statement.
4 People lie on a sunbed to get a tan.
5 People go jogging to get fit.
6 People go on a diet to lose weight.

9a)

1 Yes   2 Yes

b)

1 She began to lose weight.
2 She became more energetic.
3 She got a lot fitter.
4 She lost more weight.
5 She became more positive.
6 She got rid of her wrinkles.

c)

1 She lost weight by cutting down on alcohol.
2 She became more energetic by going out at night less.
3 She got a lot fitter by going to the gym.
4 She lost more weight by going on a diet.
5 She became more positive by buying a lot of new clothes.
6 She got rid of her wrinkles by having plastic surgery.

10

1 How about breathing into a paper bag?
2 Maybe you should tilt your head back.
3 You should put some yoghurt on it.
4 Why don't you take an aspirin?
5 You'd better put a plaster on it.
6 You must put some cold water on it.

11a)

1 c)   2 f)   3 b)
4 e)   5 a)   6 d)

b)

1 = T   2 = T   3 = F   4 = T
5 = F   6 = F

c)

1 cosmetic surgery
2 wrinkles and crow's feet
3 tinned food
4 wound
5 facial spasms
6 facelift

d)

1 You can get rid of wrinkles and crow's feet by using *Botox*.
2 You can become ill by eating tinned food which has gone off.
3 Doctors can treat some medical conditions by using botulin.
4 You can damage your face by having too many *Botox* injections.

Do you remember? Units 4–6

1

1 How long have you known Fred? — e) We've been friends for about two years.

2 When did you get here? — d) I arrived about ten minutes ago.

3 How long have you had your dog? — b) I got it about six months ago.

4 How long have you been painting portraits? — c) I started about thirty years ago. I've been doing it ever since.

5 Have you finished writing your novel? — a) No. I've done two chapters so far.

2

1 I'd buy her some flowers

2 if you promise to love me forever

3 if you asked me to

4 we won't have enough money to go on nice holidays

3

1 biggest   2 most unattractive

3 craziest   4 most expensive

5 worst

4

Crossword:

1 S, 2 EAR
3 HIP, 4 F, 5 T
HOU(L), FI, THU
6 KNEE, FIG, UM
(L), GE, B
D, 7 N, NE
8 EYEBROW, 9 W
ERC, R, 10 C
K, 11 THIGH
S, I
12 ELBOW, T, N

Extend your reading Units 4–6

1

b)

2

1 c)   2 b)   3 c)   4 a)   5 b)

3

1 e)   2 d)   3 a)   4 f)   5 c)   6 b)

4

1 figure out   2 determine   3 land

4 networking   5 acquire

5

1 artistic   2 enterprising   3 realistic

4 social   5 investigative   6 conventional

6

a) 5   b) 6   c) 1   d) 2   e) 4   f) 3

7

1 curious   2 persistent   3 ambitious

4 precise   5 self-confident   6 practical

8

How people behave with others	How people do their work
agreeable	careful
generous	efficient
honest	independent
outgoing	orderly
reserved	original
tactful	practical

Extend your grammar Units 4–6

1

1 ageless   2 fantasies   3 position

4 without   5 but   6 no   7 from

8 fashion   9 than   10 images

11 have   12 cute   13 over

14 unrealistic   15 would   16 figure

17 wider   18 might   19 forced

20 disagrees

2

1 She was finally able to get the job she wanted;

2 Finding the perfect dress for you is difficult;

3 I have been (talking) on the phone all morning;

4 Barbie is far more famous than other dolls;

5 You can lose weight by eating properly;

6 It's such a scary film that some people walk out before it's finished;

7 If I weren't so shy, I would become an actress.

8 I wish he could be here. / I wish he were here.

Extend your writing Units 4–6

1

Your address

Their name

Their address

Date

Dear Sir/Madam / Dear Mr/Ms

Body of the letter

Yours sincerely / Yours faithfully / Best wishes

Your signature

Your name

2

Your address

Their name / address

Date

Dear Ms Spencer,

I am writing in response to your advertisement for a production assistant in *The Guardian* newspaper on 26 June.

As you will see from my CV, I have a degree in History and am currently working for the travel desk of a national newspaper. I am responsible for organising the work schedule in this department. I work with a team of journalists, photographers and artists. I manage the list of current jobs and make sure that they are completed on time. This often means working late at night and at weekends.

I feel, therefore, that I have both the qualifications and experience that are necessary for the job. In addition, I would appreciate the chance to use my background in history.

Thank you for considering my application. I look forward to hearing from you.

Yours sincerely,

Your signature

Your name

7 Can we talk?

1 a)

1 a)   2 a), c), d), e), g)

3 i)   4 c), e), g), i)

5 d)   6 a), c), d), e), g)

7 c), e), i)   8 b), f)

9 d), e), g), i)   10 c), e), g), i)

11 a), d)

b)

1 got, replied to, sent   2 got, deleted

3 listen to, make, turn on, read (or open)

4 send, attach   5 writing   6 left

7 get, open (or read), delete

c)

a) access   b) attach   c) send

d) write   e) read   f) make

g) keep in touch

d)

a)   b)   d)   f)   h)

2a) and b) 🎧 (25)

The holiday was a complete disaster! On the way to the airport, we missed our train, so when we got there, the plane had left! We managed to catch a later flight, but we had to wait a long time. I was really nervous, because I'd never flown before! When we eventually got to our hotel, we found that they had given our room to another couple. Anyway, they found us a room at another hotel, and we stayed there. When I opened my suitcase, though, I realised that it wasn't mine. I'd picked up the wrong suitcase at the airport! So, I had to use my credit card, and buy some clothes. The rest of the holiday was quite nice, but the journey back was horrible! We missed our flight again, because when we got to the airport, Sophie couldn't find her passport! She'd left it at the hotel. So, we had to go back to the hotel, find the passport, and get another flight. If all of that wasn't enough, when we eventually got home, I realised I'd lost my key. I remember having it with me on the plane, so perhaps I lost it on the journey. I need another holiday to get over that one!

1 missed	2 'd left
3 managed	4 had to
5 'd never flown	6 had given
7 found	8 stayed
9 opened	10 'd picked up
11 missed	12 'd left
13 got	14 'd lost

c)
1 They missed their train.
2 The plane left .
3 They got to the airport.
4 The hotel gave their room to another couple.
5 They arrived at their hotel.
6 They went to another hotel.
7 He realised he had the wrong suitcase.
8 Sophie left her passport at the hotel.
9 They got to the airport.
10 He lost his key.
11 They arrived home.

d)

1 got	2 realised
3 had broken	4 was
5 had stolen	6 had thrown
7 thought	8 hadn't taken
9 wanted	10 realised
11 had taken	

3a) and b)
1 f) Someone had stolen everything, so he phoned the police.
2 d) My car broke down on the motorway because I'd forgotten to put petrol in it.
3 b) I didn't study the grammar, because I'd done it before.
4 c) I wasn't hungry, because I'd already had lunch.
5 a) They'd had an argument, so he bought her some flowers.
6 e) The room was empty, because everyone had gone.
7 h) I'd never flown before, so I was a bit nervous.
8 g) He didn't have any money, because he'd forgotten his wallet.

4a) and b) 🔵🔵 (25)
1 I'll phone you.
2 I'm coming to the party.
3 My computer has crashed.
4 I love you.
5 It's easy to learn English.
6 I love you, and I'll never leave you.
7 I'll phone you tomorrow.
8 It isn't a big problem, and it'll be easy to fix.

5a) 🔵🔵 (27)
So, anyway, Maria was going to have a party, on Saturday night, right, but I saw John, at work, and he told me it had been cancelled. I phoned my wife, Clarissa, and told her. She phoned Maria, who said that … no … it wasn't cancelled at all! My wife then left a message for me at work to say that she'd meet me there. Anyway, so I went straight home from work, and she wasn't there. So I waited … and waited … and she didn't turn up! I was starting to get a little worried. Then later on she came home in a taxi, and asked me where I'd been, and why I hadn't come to the party! I said that I thought it had been cancelled. The she told me that she'd left a message for me at work. Nobody had passed the message on to me, you see. Anyway, it got even more confusing, because I don't actually know Maria. But at the party, my wife was talking to a man called Rodney, and Maria thought that this man was me! We had such a laugh about it when my wife told me!

1 = T   2 = F   3 = F   4 = F
5 = T   6 = F

b)

1 John	2 Clarissa	3 Maria
4 Clarissa	5 Clarissa	6 Rodney

c)
1 John told Rodney that the party had been cancelled.
2 Clarissa asked Maria if the party had been cancelled.
3 Maria told Clarissa that the party was still on.
4 Clarissa told Maria that he wasn't her husband.
5 Clarissa asked Rodney why he hadn't come to the party.
6 Rodney told Clarissa that he thought the party had been cancelled.

6a)
He asked him if he lived in the town centre. ✓
She asked me where I worked. ✓
Corrections:
a) She asked them whether he could fix her car.
b) The journalist asked him if he thought the team would win.

c) She asked me where I lived.
d) Her asked her where she had met her boyfriend.
e) She asked them where they came from.

b)
1 Can you fix my car?
2 Do you think the team will win?
3 Do you live in the town centre?
4 Where do you work?
5 Where do you live?
6 Where did you meet your boyfriend?
7 Where do you come from?

7a) and b) 🔵🔵 (28)
1 A: Hello, Digby Communications. How can I help you?
   B: Hello, could you put me through to Mrs Dimchester?
   A: I'm afraid she's out of the office at the moment. Can you call back later?
   B: Certainly.
2 A: Hello, Kovach and Noble Advertising. Can I help you?
   B: Hello there. I'm trying to get through to Dexter Flynn. I was talking to him a moment ago, and I got cut off. Is he there?
   A: I'm afraid Mr Flynn has just gone into a meeting. Let me take down your name and number, and I'll get him to call you back later.
   B: Sorry, I can't hear you very well. Could you say that again?
   A: If you give me your name and number, he'll get back to you later.
   B: OK, thanks. It's Albert Collingwood.
3 A: Hello, I'm sorry to ring you up so late in the evening, but is Katerina there?
   B: I'm sorry, there's nobody here called Katerina. You must have the wrong number.
   A: I'm very sorry, I looked up the number in the book. Oh, he's hung up. How rude!

1 put (me) through	2 call back
3 get through	4 cut off
5 take down	6 call (you) back
7 get back	8 ring (you) up
9 looked up	10 hung up

8a), b), c) and d) 🔵🔵 (29)
(stressed syllables are underlined)
BETH: Hi there, Vanessa.
VANESSA: Hi Beth, how are you?
B: Really well, thanks. I passed my exam!
V: Fantastic! Well done!
B: Thanks. I'm going out tonight with some friends to celebrate.
V: Where are you going?
B: To that new restaurant on the high street. Do you fancy coming?
V: I'd love to. What time?
B: About seven-thirty

9a) 🔘🔘 (30)

MARIA: … so anyway, we had this big argument, and I threw him out! I haven't heard from him since.

KATE: What … you mean he hasn't phoned you?

M: No! Not at all! He's probably worried that if he does, I might go round and hit him with the phone!

K: What happened?

M: It's almost like he's married to his mobile. He called me from the train, to say he was coming over to see me. He told me he'd bought a new mobile, and that's what he was using when he rang up.

K: Uh-huh.

M: Then about twenty minutes later, he phoned again, to say he'd met a friend on the train, and that they were just having a quick beer in the pub. I was trying to watch a film …. *Pass the Salt* … and each time he rang, I had to get up and answer the phone, and I was missing all the good bits.

K: Hmm.

M: Then about half an hour later, he called again …

K: Again!

M: Yeah! To tell me he was on the bus.

K: You're joking!

M: Yeah. He said the bus was stuck in a traffic jam, so he was going to be a bit late. I said "Fine, but I'm trying to watch a film. Every time you phone me, I miss an important bit. So please, don't phone me until you get here. It sounds as if your new mobile phone works perfectly."

K: And what happened next?

M: Well, twenty minutes later, he phoned me from a florist's shop. He'd remembered that it was my mother's birthday, and so he phoned to ask me what sort of flowers she likes.

K: And did you go mad?

M: Well, no, because the film had finished by this time, and it was nice of him to remember my mum's birthday. But I was a bit annoyed that he'd phoned again when I'd asked him not to.

K: Yeah, I can understand that.

M: So, he said he'd see me in about ten minutes or so. Then the next thing I knew, the phone went again. I just picked it up, and shouted down the phone …

K: And what did Danny say?

M: Well, it wasn't him! It was my friend Lisa, who'd phoned to invite me to her brother's wedding.

K: Oh dear.

M: So, I said I was sorry, and explained that Danny kept phoning me on his mobile phone.

K: So she was OK about it?

M: Yeah, no problem. But after I'd put the phone down from talking to Lisa, it rang again!

K: Again!

M: Yeah … and guess what … it was Danny again. He thought it would be funny to phone me up again. This time he was outside my front door. By that time I'd answered the phone so many times, I just didn't see the funny side.

K: What did he say when he was outside your door?

M: Well, precisely that. "I'm outside your front door."

K: And what did you say?

M: Well, I just said "Why can't you use the doorbell like everyone else?" He explained that it was just a joke, and asked if he could come in.

K: And …

M: And so I let him in. He didn't realise that I was actually quite angry with him. Anyway, he went upstairs to use the bathroom, and … the phone rang again. He really thought it was funny. But I just got really angry. So I went upstairs, and I threw him out. I called him all the names under the sun, and told him not to call me for a week.

K: And when did this happen?

M: Well, it was a week and a half ago. I'm getting a bit worried that he might have found someone else. It's really unlike him not to try and get in touch.

K: Have you thought about phoning him?

M: Yeah….but

K: I think you should. He's nice, really. He's just a bit too fond of his telephone.

M: I think you're right. I'm going to give him a ring. Can I borrow your mobile?

1b)   2b)

b)

1 a)   2 b)   3 c)   4 b)   5 b)   6 a)

c)

1 because c)   2 so d)   3 so a)
4 so e)   5 because g)   6 because b)
7 because f)

d)

1 Danny phoned again to tell Maria that he'd met a friend.

2 Danny had remembered that it was Maria's mother's birthday, so he phoned from the florist's.

3 When Danny phoned from the florist's, the film had finished.

4 Lisa had phoned because she wanted to invite Maria to a wedding.

5 I'd answered the phone so many times that I didn't see the funny side.

8 Life, death and the universe

1a)

1 It definitely won't happen.
2 It probably won't happen.
3 It might not happen.
4 It might happen.
5 It'll probably happen.
6 It'll definitely happen.

b)

1 We're all going to die! The asteroid is heading straight for Earth!

2 She's going to hit him. She's really annoyed.

3 That car's going to crash! It's going straight towards the wall.

4 His trousers are going to fall down. I've seen this film before.

5 She's going to have a baby. Her tummy is very big.

6 David's going to teach us how to talk about the future. I saw his timetable on his desk.

c)

1 e) The Bujunga language is going to disappear.
2 a) Anna's going to be late.
3 b) They'll meet again before the end.
4 d) Trevor's going to get married.
5 c) There's going to be an election.

2a) 🔘🔘 (31)

JOHN: So, what's the programme about, Jane?

JANE: Well, ten people go into a house, and live together for nine weeks.

JOHN: What, ten of them, for nine weeks?

JANE: No, each week, one of them has to leave.

JOHN: And how do they decide who leaves?

JANE: All of the people in the house vote each week, to decide which two people should go.

JOHN: Two people? I thought you said only one had to leave.

JANE: Oh yes. The viewers vote which of those two should go.

JOHN: And how do we decide?

JANE: Well, it's on the TV every night, and you can also go to the *In the House* website, on the Internet. You can vote on the website, or you can phone a special number.

JOHN: I've never heard of anything so dull in all my life! Who'd want to watch a load of strangers trying to live together? I'm not going to watch any of it.

JANE: Well I'm going to watch it every night. I think it'll be really fascinating. And I bet you'll get interested in it.

JOHN: No way! I'm not going to watch it at all.

JANE: You will … You will …

1 c)   2 a)

b)

1 b)   2 b)   3 No   4 c)   5 Yes

c) and d) (32)

JOHN: Oh, no! Patty has to leave the house! She's been voted out! Look, I think she's going to start crying.

JANE: No, she isn't going to cry, she's just got something in her eye.

JOHN: I read in the newspaper that she's going to record a song when she comes out.

JANE: Oh, dear. That's a bad idea. It'll probably be awful.

JOHN: What about Matty? What do you think will happen to him?

JANE: I'm not sure. But he definitely won't stay in the house until the end. In fact, I think the viewers will probably vote him out next weekend.

JOHN: Maybe, maybe not. We'll see when the time comes.

JANE: I think Hattie might stay a bit longer. I think she'll still be there next week.

JOHN: Yes, you're right. But she's starting to annoy the other contestants. Hey look! She's going to kiss Matty! No! I was wrong. She's going to kiss Warren.

JANE: Oh! She's so annoying! Anyway. You told me you weren't going to watch this programme!

JOHN: No, I said I *might* not watch it.

1 's going to   2 isn't going to
3 's going to   4 'll   5 will   6 won't
7 will   8 'll   9 'll   10 's going to
11 's going to   12 weren't going to

3

1 a) Don't forget to video the evening news, otherwise you won't see your brother talking to that pop star.
   b) Don't forget to video the evening news, in case your brother's on it.

2 a) I'll take some cash with me in case they don't take credit cards.
   b) I'll take some cash with me, otherwise I won't be able to pay!

3 a) We'd better not walk, otherwise we won't get there on time.
   b) We'd better not walk, in case it's a long way.

4 a) I'll bring the key in case you want to look around the new house.
   b) I'll bring the key, otherwise you won't be able to look around.

5 a) I'm going to study the Present Perfect in case it comes up in the test.
   b) I'm going to study the Present Perfect, otherwise I won't know it for the test.

4a)

1 If I hadn't felt stressed all the time, I wouldn't have argued with my boss.
2 If I hadn't argued with my boss, I wouldn't have lost my job.
3 If I hadn't lost my job, I wouldn't have argued with my wife.
4 If I hadn't argued with my wife, she wouldn't have left me.
5 If my wife hadn't left me, I wouldn't have lost interest in life.
6 If I hadn't lost interest in life, I wouldn't have ended up here.
7 If I hadn't ended up here, I wouldn't have met Ida.

b)

1 If I hadn't met Ida, I wouldn't have felt happy.
2 If I hadn't felt happy, I wouldn't have become interested in life again.
3 If I hadn't become interested in life again, I wouldn't have found a job.
4 If I hadn't found a job, I wouldn't have earned some money.
5 If I hadn't earned some money, I wouldn't have been able to invest it.
6 If I hadn't been able to invest the money, I wouldn't have become rich.
7 If I hadn't become rich, I wouldn't have bought a big house.

5

1 blame   2 relief   3 regret
4 blame   5 relief   6 regret

6a), b) and c) (33)

1 If I'd <u>seen</u> him, I would have <u>told</u> him. [w]
2 I <u>haven't</u> seen <u>John</u> yet. Have <u>you</u>? [s, s]
3 <u>What</u> <u>time</u> did you have <u>dinner</u> last night? [s]
4 I'm <u>sure</u> I would have <u>seen</u> her if she'd <u>been</u> there. [w]
5 Have you <u>done</u> your <u>homework</u> yet? [s]
6 You <u>wouldn't</u> have <u>lost</u> your <u>job</u> if you hadn't <u>shouted</u> at the <u>boss</u>. [w]

7a)

1 = T   2 = F   3 = F   4 = T

b)

1 = R   2 = W   3 = R   4 = W

8a) and b) (34)

1 A: Please, we need one more player to complete the team.
   B: Well, I'm not sure.
   A: Be a sport
2 A: You've got to tell him.
   B: But he'll be really shocked!
   A: If you ask me, you haven't got any choice.

3 A: I really don't want to, OK?
   B: Don't be such a wimp. It won't bite.
   A: You must be joking. Look at those teeth.
   B: Look. I'll do it. Aaaaaaargh!
4 A: It's quite a small car.
   B: It's big enough for us and the children. And your mother.
   A: I don't think so. We've got six children, remember?
   B: I see your point.

c)

a) 4   b) 2   c) 3   d) 1

9a)

1 f)   2 a)   3 c)   4 d)   5 b)   6 e)

b)

a) If Jim hadn't told the organisers to announce my name, I wouldn't have got up to sing.
b) If I hadn't got up to sing when they announced my name, I would have felt stupid.
c) If I hadn't got up to sing, I wouldn't have realised I was a good singer.
d) If I hadn't released a CD, I wouldn't have had enough money to buy good equipment.
e) If I hadn't invested my money in good equipment, my karaoke nights wouldn't have become successful.

c) and d)

a) B 2   b) B 4   c) J 3   d) J 5   e) J 1

9 It's a family affair

1

2a) and b) (35)

The Family Party

The party was father's idea
He was missing his long-lost relations
His cousins, their mothers, their sisters and brothers
Who all lived in various nations.
My mother sent out invitations
The replies were quite slow coming back
And one from Romania, postmarked "Transylvania"

Had a smear of blood on the back.
They hired a marquee for the garden
And a couple of chefs for the food
A group of musicians, a pair of magicians
And a comedian who wasn't too rude.
And then on the day of the party
There were friends from all over the planet
And one or two strangers, who presented
no danger
And a small chimpanzee, called Janet.
The decorations looked lovely
And people bought gifts for the host
There was champagne and cake, some
chicken and steak
And caviar, olives and toast.
But families bring complications
And an argument started quite soon
Between great-uncle Bert, who got wine on
his shirt
And my cousin's great-aunty, called June.
Then everything seemed to go wrong
Food and drink flew through the air
A big loaf of bread hit my dad on the head
Followed quite soon by a chair.
When the guests left, there was silence
My father sat, drinking a beer
With his hands on his head, then he
suddenly said
"Shall we do it again, every year?"

3a)
1 We shouldn't have come here.
2 I should have listened to my mother.
3 I shouldn't have become a teacher.
4 I should have had my car serviced.
5 I shouldn't have started smoking.
6 I should have read the invitation.

b)
1 We should never have come here.
2 I should never have become a teacher.
3 I should never have started smoking.

c)
1 If only we had gone somewhere else.
2 I wish I'd married Bud instead.
3 If only I'd finished my marking earlier.
4 I wish I'd bought a different car.
5 If only I'd given up when I was younger.
6 I wish I'd asked if it was fancy dress.

d)
1 b)   2 e)   3 a)   4 f)   5 c)   6 d)
1 If we hadn't gone to that bar, my wife
  wouldn't have discovered us.
2 If I'd listened to my mother, I wouldn't
  have married him.
3 If I hadn't become a teacher, I wouldn't
  have so much work.
4 If I'd had my car serviced, it wouldn't
  have broken down.
5 If I hadn't started smoking, I wouldn't
  find it difficult to give up.

6 If I'd read the invitation, I wouldn't have
  gone in fancy dress.
  (Present tense is used in the second
  part of sentences 3 and 5.)

4a)
1 for, because, so that
2 because of, in order to, because
3 because, so that, for
4 for, because, in order to

b)
1 we came to this pub
2 his laziness
3 it doesn't pay very well
4 it keeps breaking down

c)
2 I love him even though / although he's lazy.
3 I love teaching despite / in spite of the
  money.
4 I love my car despite / in spite of the fact
  that it isn't reliable.

5a)
a) = T   b) = T   c) = F   d) = F   e) = T

b)
1 become	2 receive	3 obtain
4 obtain	5 obtain	6 receive
7 become	8 become	9 become
10 arrive	11 become	12 take

6a) ⊙⊙ (36)
I can't stand my brother Patrick. He's
always complaining, for a start. He doesn't
like his dinner, or he doesn't want to take
the dog for a walk. And he never helps with
the washing up. He always finds something
else to do when it's his turn. He's always
using my things, too, like my CDs, or my
pens and pencils. I don't mind if he asks
me first, and if he promises to be careful
with them. But I'm sick of him just taking
them. And I'm fed up with him not putting
things back, too. And then there's my
bicycle! I never get the chance to use it,
because he's always on it. If he asked, I
wouldn't mind, but he never does. And I'm
tired of him making a noise all the time,
too. I can't concentrate when I'm trying to
do my homework, because he's always
running around shouting and being …
well, just being a boy! And he annoys my
friends, too, when they come round. He
won't leave us alone. They're all fed up with
him, too. He drives me mad! Boys are
horrible!

1 = T   2 a) = T, b) = T, c) = F
3 = T   4 = F   5 = F   6 = F   7 = F

b)
1 He's always complaining.
2 He never helps with the washing up.
3 He's always using my things.
4 I'm sick of him just taking them.

5 I'm fed up with him not putting things
  back.
6 I'm tired of him making a noise all the
  time.
7 He's always running around shouting.

c)
1 always	2 fed up
3 sick	4 never
5 always	6 fed up

7
2 You're always leaving your homework
  until Sunday evening!
3 I'm sick of you accusing me of not
  listening!
4 You never want to talk about your
  feelings!
5 You're always borrowing my CDs. You
  never ask!
6 You're always using the telephone! You
  never help to pay the bill!
7 You never let me watch football!
8 I'm fed up with you telling awful jokes to
  my friends!
9 I'm sick of you coming home late! You
  never tell me where you're going!
10 I'm tired of telling you to tidy your room!

8a), b) and c) ⊙⊙ (37)
1 You're my cousin's wife, aren't you? [F]
2 You've had your hair cut, haven't you? [F]
3 You can speak Japanese, can't you? [R]
4 You didn't drink my beer my mistake, did
  you? [R]
5 You haven't seen my wife, have you? [R]
6 You aren't the same Jay Hawkins I went
  to school with, are you? [R]
7 I'm next, aren't I? [R]

9
1 ✗ I shouldn't have stayed out so late last
  night. I'm tired!
2 ✓
3 ✗ I wish I hadn't met you. You only make
  me sad.
4 ✗ If only I had sent the invitations for the
  party out on time! Nobody will come!
5 ✗ If I had sent the invitations out on time,
  everybody would have come. Now it's too
  late!
6 ✓
7 ✗ I wish I had put on some warm
  clothes. I'm freezing!
8 ✗ He's so annoying! He's always asking
  me silly questions.
9 ✗ I'm sick of you asking me silly
  questions all the time.
10 ✗ You never do the washing up! Why do
  I always have to do it?
11 ✓
12 ✗ I'm going to ask my boss for a
  holiday, because I need a rest.

10a) 🔊 (38)

When he first came into my life, I don't think I was ready for him. I was a busy woman, I was hardly ever at home, and I don't think I gave him the attention he needed. I kept thinking to myself "I should never have fallen in love with you. If only we'd met at a different time." But he was so good to me, and so affectionate that in spite of his bad points, I wanted us to be together. Oh, but he's got some irritating habits. I'm fed up with clearing up after him all the time. He's so messy, and he doesn't even seem to realise! And he's always making a noise when I'm trying to watch something on the television. I get so fed up with this that I just switch it off. And I'm getting tired of not knowing where he is. Sometimes, when he goes out in the morning he doesn't get home again until really late at night, and it's impossible to find out where he's been.

I'll never forget the day I thought he'd gone forever. We were on the beach, having a wonderful time, running around, or sitting and looking at the waves crashing onto the shore. He went into the sea, and he was swimming about. Suddenly it seemed as though he was having difficulties, and he couldn't swim back to the beach. He just got further and further away, until I couldn't see him any more.

Immediately I began to regret all the horrible things I'd ever said to him. I was thinking things like "If only I'd been nicer to you", and "I wish I'd been at home more", and "I should have given you more affection". I thought I'd never see him again. I thought about his face, his ears, his nose, and his big, beautiful brown eyes. In the end, they sent a helicopter out to look for him, and it was such a relief when they found him, and rescued him from the sea. I'll never forget how he ran towards me from the helicopter, jumped up and licked my face all over. He's such a wonderful dog, I could never live without him despite his bad points.

1 c)   2 a)   3 b)   4 b)
5 c)   6 b)   7 b)   8 c)

b) 🔊 (39)

I'm always getting complaints about him from the neighbours. A lot of people in the area have cats, and of course, being cats, he doesn't like them so, he's always chasing them! He's always chasing the postman, too, and tries to bite him. Sometimes I get fed up with him lying on the sofa, or on the armchairs when I'm not looking. He's not supposed to do that, and he knows it. And

I'm getting tired of finding him sitting on the end of my bed every morning. He wakes me up before my alarm clock goes off, and that's the last thing I want, first thing in the morning. And if he's been out in the rain, or swimming in a river, or something, he's always shaking himself, so I get soaking wet!

c)

Ticked sentences are:

1, 3, 5, 6

d)

1 I should never have fallen in love with you.
2 If only we'd met at a different time.
3 If only I'd been nicer to you.
4 I wish I'd been at home more.
5 I should have given you more affection.

e)

1 I wanted us to be together although he has some bad points.
2 … despite his bad points.
3 … because he is affectionate.
4 … because of the affection he shows me.

Do you remember? Units 7–9

1a)

1 woke up
2 'd forgotten
3 rushed
4 didn't have
5 'd forgotten
6 ironed
7 got
8 'd left
9 went
10 got back
11 had been cancelled
12 got to
13 had left
14 had broken down
15 had gone
16 went
17 didn't have
18 had done
19 had gone
20 had left

b)

1 so   2 so   3 because
4 because   5 so

2

1 I told her I'd bought her some flowers.
2 "I don't really like them."
3 "I've bought you ones like this before."
4 She said that I hadn't, and that I was thinking of someone else.

3

1 Kevin would have known where the party was if Tracy hadn't forgotten to tell him about it.
2 If I'd known you were coming home early, I would have made you something to eat.
3 I wouldn't have been hungry all afternoon if I'd had some lunch.
4 If you'd given me proper directions, I would have got there on time.

Extend your reading Units 7–9

2

2 i)   3 a)   4 e)   5 j)   6 h)
7 c)   8 b)

3

1 c)   2 a)   3 a)   4 b)   5 c)

4

1 f)   2 a)   3 e)   4 h)
5 b)   6 g)   7 c)   8 d)

5 and 6

1 a)   2 b)   3 c)

7

1 Italy
2 It will go up.
3 It increases the number.
4 Nobody knows why.
5 They crashed because 13 million people tried to make calls.

8

1 sign up   2 per capita   3 household
4 push … up   5 clock off

Extend your grammar Units 7–9

1

1 going
2 so
3 this
4 As
5 of
6 felt
7 by
8 towards
9 where
10 suddenly
11 caught
12 no
13 into
14 itself
15 before
16 him
17 thing
18 one
19 Once
20 It

2

1 the line (in order) to put me
2 who got married last Saturday was
3 not likely to have
4 was believed to
5 promised to call home if there was
6 don't have as many children as
7 had known you had to send a fax, I would have offered you
8 should have left a message

Extend your writing Units 7–9

1 a) and b)

Can you give me a lift?

At 10 o'clock on a **gloomy** November evening in downtown Seattle, an **attractive young** woman (returned / <u>was returning</u>) to her car when a **handsome** man (had come / <u>came</u>) and spoke to her. At the time she (felt / <u>was feeling</u>) rather afraid because she (just saw / <u>had just seen</u>) a **spine-chilling** horror movie. The man (was explaining / <u>explained</u>) that earlier that evening he (was seeing / <u>had seen</u>) some **suspicious-looking** children around her car and (was deciding / <u>had decided</u>) to look after it for her. He (had said / <u>said</u>) that **unfortunately** because of this he (was missing / <u>had missed</u>) the last train home. He **politely** (<u>asked</u> / was asking) her for a lift home. At first she **understandably** (had felt / <u>felt</u>) a bit worried but after a few moments, she

hesitantly (was agreeing / agreed).
It (was / had been) a **bitterly** cold night but **suddenly** she (was noticing / noticed) sweat on his face and she (had started / started) to worry. Why (was he / had he been) so **obviously** nervous? **Alarmed**, she (asked / was asking) him to get out of the car and direct her out of the parking lot. As he **carefully** (showed / was showing) her the way out, she (was driving / drove) away **at high speed** leaving him behind.
Ten minutes later, after she (calmed / had calmed) down, she (was noticing / noticed) that he (left / had left) his **battered** briefcase on the floor of the car. She (was stopping / stopped) and, **shaking with fear**, (opened / was opening) it. Inside, as she (was looking/looked) through his books and papers, **to her horror** she (found/ had found) a long knife with a bloody blade!

10 What's going on?
1

2a) and b) 〔OO〕 (40)
1 World famous football team Tadchester City were beaten yesterday by a team from the village of Bottomley. Tadchester City star player Danny Beckenham said it was unfair that Bottomley were given a penalty two minutes from the end of the match. He also said that he saw Bottomley player Ted Farmer give the referee some money before the match.
2 Top computer company Macrostuff was bought yesterday by the billionaire media tycoon Robert Mardock for $20 billion. The value of Macrostuff went up by 20 per cent, and the founder of the company, William Dawes, has retired, saying he is looking forward to never working again. Dawes invented the computer programme "Fenestro", which is used on most of the world's personal computers.
3 Singing star Alvin Parsley was injured last night when an item of women's clothing was thrown onto the stage during a concert. The clothing landed on Parsley's head, and he was unable to see properly. A member of the audience was taken to hospital also, after the singer landed on her when he fell off the stage.

4 Famous criminal Violet Crabbe was released from prison yesterday after thirty years. Crabbe and her sister Veronica were imprisoned for their part in The Great Bus Robbery, and for the murder of their friend Jackie "the Bump" Rowntree. Rowntree's body was found under a motorway, when drivers noticed that the surface of the road wasn't flat.
1: 1 were beaten, 2 were given, 3 saw
2: 1 was bought, 2 went up, 3 has retired, 4 invented, 5 is used
3: 1 was injured, 2 was thrown, 3 was taken
4: 1 was released, 2 was found, 3 noticed
c)
1 b)   2 b)   3 a)   4 b)   5 a)
6 b)   7 a)   8 a)
d)
1 Macrostuff was bought by Robert Mardock for $20 billion.
2 "Fenestro" is used by most people who own a computer.
3 Something was thrown onto the stage during Alvin's concert.
4 The injured member of the audience was taken to hospital.
5 Jackie "the Bump" Rowntree's body was found by the police.
6 The police were told by drivers that the road wasn't flat.
3a) 〔OO〕 (41)
I was born on July 31st, 1935, in London. I went to Ardnock School near my home, but I'm afraid I left when I was sixteen, without getting any qualifications. My first contact with the police was the week after I left school, when they arrested me for stealing sweets from a local shop. That's how I started my career as a criminal. Then in 1970, a gang of criminals carried out the Great Bus Robbery, in South London. The police couldn't find out who was responsible, but then the next year, 1971, they arrested me, and accused me of organising it! I was found guilty, though I swear it wasn't me, and the same year, I went to Parkville Prison. In 1972, my dear sister, Veronica, helped me to escape from prison, and I remained free until 1974. However, the year before that, in 1973, someone killed our friend Jackie Rowntree, who became known as "the Bump" when she was found dead under a new motorway. It wasn't me who killed her, honest, I'm completely innocent, but the police arrested me the year after the murder, and sent me back to prison! Anyway, I haven't wasted my time inside. I've been writing my autobiography, called *It wasn't me*. I was released last week, and the book will be released next week.

1 Date of Birth: July 31st, 1945
2 Left Ardnock school
3 First arrested by police: aged sixteen; crime: stealing sweets
4 A gang of criminals carried out the Great Bus Robbery. 1970
5 The police arrested her, and accused her of organising the robbery. 1971
6 She went to Parkville prison. 1971
7 Veronica Crabbe helped her to escape from prison. 1972
8 Someone killed Jackie "the Bump" Rowntree. 1973
9 The police arrested Violet. She went to prison for the murder. 1974
10 She came out of prison.
11 Her autobiography (*It wasn't me*) comes out.
b)
1 She was arrested for the first time when she was sixteen years old.
2 She was arrested in 1971 and accused of organising the Great Bus Robbery.
3 She was helped to escape by her sister Veronica.
4 She was released from prison last week.
5 Her autobiography will be released next week.
4a)
1 be released   2 be told
3 being invited   4 to be given
5 being given   6 to be disturbed
7 to be trained   8 be encouraged
b)
1 got arrested   2 got hit
3 got trapped   4 got knocked
5 got wrecked   6 got hurt
c)
1 I was told to come and see you.
2 I was told to ask for Mr Grimsdale.
3 I wasn't told it was a fancy dress party.
4 Why wasn't I informed?
5
1 drink driving   2 fiddling expenses
3 shoplifting   4 burglary
5 forgery   6 fraud
6a) and b) 〔OO〕 (42)
(stressed syllables in bold)
1 c) Don't you want some more <u>cake</u>?
2 f) Weren't you frightened by the <u>film</u>?
3 g) Haven't we met somewhere be<u>fore</u>?
4 e) Shouldn't you be at <u>work</u>?
5 b) Isn't she a famous <u>film</u> star?
6 d) Didn't we see that man on <u>TV</u> yesterday?
7 a) Weren't you my <u>tea</u>cher?
b)
b) The speaker's voice stays level from the start of the sentence to the final stressed syllable.

7a) and b)

1 It's against the rules to smoke in this building. / Smoking in this building isn't allowed.
2 It's illegal to murder someone. / Murdering someone is against the law.
3 It's rude to point at people. / Pointing at people is rude.
4 It's illegal to burgle a house. / Burgling a house is against the law.
5 It's rude to belch after a meal. / Belching after a meal is anti-social.
6 It's rude to pick your nose in public. / Picking your nose in public is anti-social.
7 It's against the rules to take flash photos in the theatre. / Taking flash photos in the cinema isn't allowed.

8a)

1 e)   2 f)   3 a)   4 b)
5 c)   6 g)   7 d)   8 h)

b) 🎧 **(43)**

PRESENTER: And now to finish today's programme, we have our legal expert Sue Quickly, who's going to tell us all about the strange laws which exist in various parts of the world. Is it true, Sue, that drivers in Greece can be sent to prison for not wearing smart clothes?

SUE: Well, not sent to prison, exactly, but it is still theoretically an offence for which you can be fined. However, I'm not sure that the Greek police would actually enforce it.

P: And is that the case with many of these strange laws, that they are old laws which have simply never been changed?

S: Yes, that's right. For most of these you're unlikely to get into trouble, and many of them date back a long time.

P: Are there any strange laws for which we do know the reason?

S: Yes, for example, in Fairbanks, Alaska, it is illegal for a moose to walk along the pavement.

P: A moose? Why would a moose want to walk along the pavement? And who would arrest the poor animal?

S: You see this one dates back to the time when Fairbanks was a small town with very few people living there. The owner of one particular bar apparently had a pet moose, which he brought into the bar, and gave it beer to drink. The moose would get drunk, and walk around the town being ... well, being rather dangerous, I would think!

P: Mmm, yes.

S: And you see in order to get into the bar in the first place, the moose had to go across the pavement.

P: I see, and so with the law in place, the owner couldn't get the animal into the bar in the first place.

S: That's right.

P: And are there any others with a reason, like that one?

S: Well, in Singapore, there is a fine if you don't flush the toilet after using it. Clearly public hygiene is the reason here.

P: Uh-huh, that makes sense.

S: Some laws have their origin in religion, too. For example, children in Ottawa, Canada, can't eat icecream on the street on Sundays.

P: But there are also some which are completely absurd, aren't there?

S: Yes, for example, again in Alaska, you can shoot bears, in the right season, and with a licence, but you aren't allowed to wake them up in order to take a photograph of them!

P: Wake up a sleeping bear ... ha ha ha!

S: And in Michigan, in the USA, it is illegal to tie an alligator to a fire hydrant.

P: As you do ...

S: In Massachusetts, again in the USA, you have to have a licence to wear a goatee beard ... other types of beard are fine, though.

P: That's a prickly one ...

S: But the strangest one of all is an old law in Britain, which made it illegal to try to kill yourself.

P: Well, maybe that's not so strange. It is, after all, an offence to try to kill anyone ...

S: Yes, but the strange thing here is that the penalty for trying to commit suicide was ... execution.

P: So you could be killed for trying to kill yourself?

S: That's right.

P: How very absurd! Anyway, thank you, Sue. Fascinating stuff. See you again next week?

S: Yes, sure. I'll be here.

P: And now before the news it's over to Terry for the weekend weather...

1 e)   2 f)   3 d)   4 c)   5 g)
6 b)   7 h)   8 a)

c)

1 be fined   2 can't be fined   3 be fined
4 can't   5 can't   6 can't   7 don't need
8 executed

d)

1 It is against the law in Fairbanks to let a moose walk on the pavement.
2 You must flush the toilet in Singapore.
3 Eating ice cream on a Sunday in Ottawa isn't allowed.
4 Waking up a sleeping bear in Alaska is illegal.
5 You mustn't tie an alligator to a fire hydrant in Michigan.
6 Wearing a goatee beard without a licence is against the law in Massachusetts.
7 Killing yourself in Britain used to be illegal.

11 The silver screen

1a)

1 foyer   2 usher   3 seat
4 front row   5 screen   6 back row
7 aisle   8 audience

b) and c) 🎧 **(44)**

My favourite film is called *Rocky Island*. It's a black and white film, and it was made in 1952. It stars the American actor Dirk Stroganoff and the French-Canadian actress Candide Demure. It's set on a small island off the coast of Florida, just after the Second World War.

It was directed by Burt Madison, who also made *Rocky Island II: Love on the Rocks*. It was a big commercial success at the time, and many film critics still say it is one of the best films ever made. There aren't many special effects, but Dirk Stroganoff did all his own stunts. There aren't any car chases, because it's set on a small island, and there weren't many roads there; I suppose it's more of a psychological thriller, as there is a murder involved, but it's also a very romantic film, as the two main characters fall in love. Since then, it's been dubbed into about fourteen different languages, and there are other versions in English, but with subtitles.

1 black and white   2 made
3 stars   4 actress
5 set   6 directed
7 commercial   8 critics
9 special effects   10 stunts
11 thriller   12 romantic
13 dubbed   14 versions
15 subtitles

2

1 Every   2 all   3 whole
4 whole   5 every   6 whole

3a)

1 f)   2 b)   3 a)   4 e)   5 c)   6 d)

b)

1 = T   2 = F   3 = T   4 = F   5 = F   6 = T

c)

1 portrays
2 role
3 commercial success
4 supporting actor

4a)

1 asked	2 told	3 warned
4 asked	5 refused	6 offered
7 refused	8 agreed	9 promised

b) 🔘 **(45)**

MARIA: Oh, Jake! I've been waiting for this day for so long! But please, don't do anything to harm Luke before we leave.

JAKE: Well, Maria, it's like this. Luke owes me money. I'm gonna shoot him.

M: Oh, please, Jake. He's a good man. Leave him here in peace.

J: Listen, I'll leave him in peace if you'll marry me.

M: I thought you'd never ask. I've already chosen a dress. And my mother can help with the invitations. Then there's the wedding reception to think about … oh! there's so much to do!

J: Forget all that. I want to take you to California. We can get married there, and start a new life. Away from all … all the bad things that have happened.

M: Fine. What are we waiting for? Let's go. I'll get the horses.

1 = F   2 = F   3 = T   4 = F   5 = T   6 = F

c)

1 Jake promised to leave Luke in peace if Maria married him.
2 Jake wanted Maria to marry him.
3 Maria agreed to marry him.
4 Jake wanted her to go to California with him.
5 Maria wanted a big wedding with all her relatives.

5

1 so	2 such a	3 such
4 so	5 so	6 such
7 such a, so	8 such, such	

6a) and b) 🔘 **(46)**

1 Would you mind opening the door for me?
   Not at all. Allow me.
2 Do you mind if I open the window?
   Of course not. Please go ahead.
3 Could I have two first class stamps, please?
   Certainly, madam. Here you are.
4 Could you put me through to Mr Timpkins?
   Certainly, madam. Please hold the line.
5 Is it all right if I sit here?
   Sorry, I'm afraid it isn't free.
6 Could I have that blue armchair over there?
   Certainly. Are you paying by credit card?
7 Can I use your phone, John?
   Sure, go ahead.
8 Do you mind if I use your mobile phone, madam?
   But I don't even know you!

1 R b)	2 P d)	3 R a)	4 R e)
5 P c)	6 R h)	7 P f)	8 P g)

7a), b), c), d) and e) 🔘 **(47)**

1 Would you mind opening the <u>door</u> for me? (No, not at all. ✓)
2 Can I borrow your <u>pen</u>? (Yes, go ahead. ✓)
3 Excuse me, is anyone <u>sitting</u> here? (Yes, I'm afraid it's taken.)
4 Do you mind if I open the <u>window</u>? (No, of course not. ✓)
5 Can I open the <u>window</u>? (Yes, please do. ✓)
6 Is it all right if I <u>sit</u> here? (Yes, please go ahead. ✓)
7 Do you mind if I borrow your <u>pen</u>? (No, of course not. ✓)
8 Could I possibly borrow your <u>pen</u>? (Yes, of course. ✓)

e)

1 = P	2 = I	3 = P	4 = P	5 = I
6 = I	7 = P	8 = P	9 = I	

8a) and b) 🔘 **(48)**

1 Do you mind if I smoke?
   I'd prefer it if you didn't. It makes me cough.
2 Could I possibly borrow £10,000?
   I'm afraid I can't authorise any more lending.
3 Is it okay if I sit here?
   I'm afraid it's taken.
4 Do you mind if I open the window?
   I'd prefer it if you didn't. I'm feeling cold.
5 Do you mind if I dance with your husband?
   I'm afraid he's hurt his leg.
6 Can I borrow your car, Dad?
   Actually, I was going to use it myself.

1 c)   2 f)   3 e)   4 a)   5 d)   6 b)

9a)

1 b)   2 b)   3 a)

b)

1 Mary Shelley
2 Switzerland
3 To index Count Dracula's library
4 Jonathan Harker's girlfriend
5 Professor van Helsing
6 Sir Henry Baskerville
7 The hound from Hell

12 Taking off

1a) and b) 🔘 **(49)**

1 My favourite holiday was in Paris, a couple of years ago. I really love seeing the sights. We went to the Eiffel Tower, the Louvre, the Arc de Triomphe. We saw everything! I love buying souvenirs, too. I got a lovely little model of the Eiffel Tower. I gave it to my mother.
2 I went to Ibiza last year, and had a great time! There's such great nightlife there that I didn't actually see much of the

place we stayed in! We went clubbing all night, and just chilled out in the day in the hotel. We were on a budget, so we couldn't do anything too expensive. We saved our money for the clubs.
3 I'm going to work my way round South America. I've taken a course in how to teach English, and I'm going to use that to help me travel. I'm going to go to unusual places, a bit off the beaten track. I don't like places where you just meet lots of people from your own country. I want to take risks, and live a little dangerously.

1 seeing the sights, souvenirs
2 great nightlife, chilled out, on a budget
3 work my way, off the beaten track, take risks

2

1 b)   2 b)   3 c)   4 c)

3a), b) and c) 🔘 **(50)**

TREVOR: It could be the Hotel Berlin, because there is a restaurant next door. What do you think, Mary?

MARY: Well, it can't be the Hotel Berlin, Trevor, because there isn't a swimming pool on the roof.

T: How about the Hotel Bueno … it might be that one.

M: I don't think so, Trevor. It can't be the Bueno, because it isn't family-run. Look, it says there are other Hotel Buenos. Lots of them, in fact. It could be the Hotel Bali, though.

T: The Bali? No, it doesn't look very friendly to me, Mary. Look, that man's getting kicked out.

M: But there is a restaurant next door.

T: That's true. How about the Biarritz, though, Mary? That's a possibility.

M: No! It can't be! It isn't finished yet!

T: But it begins with a 'B'… It could be … Oh, I hope not.

M: Hang on. What's the name of this town?

T: It's Puerto Grande.

M: Oh no! We're meant to be going to Puerto Industrial! We must have got on the wrong bus!

T: Are you sure? Oh dear! I told you we should have got a taxi …

1 Hotel Berlin
   It could be the Hotel Berlin, because there is a restaurant next door.
   It can't be the Hotel Berlin, because there isn't a swimming pool on the roof.
2 Hotel Bueno
   It might be the Hotel Bueno because there is a swimming pool on the roof.
   It can't be the Hotel Bueno, because it isn't family-run.

3 Hotel Bali
It might not be the Hotel Bali, because it doesn't look very friendly.
It could be the Hotel Bali because there is a swimming pool on the roof and there is a restaurant next door.
4 Hotel Biarritz
It can't be the Hotel Biarritz, because it isn't finished yet.
It might be the Hotel Biarritz because it begins with a 'B'!

c)
1 = T   2 = M   3 = T   4 = M   5 = M
6 = T   7 = T   8 = M   9 = M

4a) and b) 🎧 (51)
PRESENTER: Welcome to this week's edition of *What on earth is it?*, the programme where we decide what strange objects were designed for. And I'd like also to welcome my guest this week, Sir Arthur Expert, an antique dealer. Hello, Sir Arthur.
A: Hello, Penelope.
P: Let's look at this week's first object. Sir Arthur, can you describe it for us? And remember, listeners, that you can see this week's strange objects on our website, www.whatonearthisit.com. So, Sir Arthur, what's the first thing you have for us this week?
A: Well, it's made of wood and leather, it's about 30cm high and 20cm wide, and cylindrical in shape.
P: It looks absolutely fascinating. Where is it from?
A: I'm not exactly sure. It was sent in by a lady from South London, who was given it by her grandmother, who once lived in Egypt. So, there's a good chance that it comes from North Africa.
P: What are those funny metal things on the top?
A: Well, if we suppose that it's a musical instrument of some sort, then they might be used to make sure it's in tune. Look, if you turn them, and then hit it, the sound changes.
P: Can you demonstrate for us?
A: I ... er ... need something to hit it with.
P: Here, use my pen.
P: Try turning the metal things again. Oops.
A: Oh, I say! Oh dear!
P: Is it broken?
A: Er ... no, I don't think so. I think I can fix it if I just ... there, that's better.
P: Is it definitely a musical instrument?
A: That seems to be the most logical conclusion. However, there are some

holes down here which suggest that it might have been used for other purposes.
P: Such as … ?
A: Well, possibly for making butter.
P: Butter!
A: Yes, maybe you put the milk in here, turn it around a bit, and hey presto! Lovely butter!
P: Do you have any other ideas?
A: Yes. Perhaps it was used in … er … wedding ceremonies…er…as a kind of … er … a kind of a … thing … to … er … stand on. Or something.
P: You don't actually know, do you?
A: Er … yes, er … um … that's what it is. It's a … wedding stool … For short men to stand on. Next to the … tall person they're going to get married to.
P: Call yourself an expert? You haven't got a clue, have you!
A: Er … um … it could be a …
1 = Yes   2 = a)

b)
1 = F   2 = F   3 = T   4 = T   5 = T   6 = T

5a) and b) 🎧 (52)
1 A: He must be Spanish.
  B: He can't be Spanish. He's got blue eyes!
2 A: It could be a kind of chair.
  B: It can't be a kind of chair. It's really uncomfortable!
3 A: They might have gone on holiday.
  B: They can't have gone on holiday. I saw them an hour ago.
4 A: They can't be married!
  B: They must be. They're wearing rings.
5 A: She could have gone to the shops.
  B: She can't have gone to the shops. She's left the door open!

6a
1 ✓   2 ✓   3 ✗   4 ✓   5 ✗   6 ✗

b)
1 You can't be hungry! You've just eaten everything in the fridge!
2 I don't know what it is. It might be a musical instrument, or it might be a chair.
3 It can't be a chair! It looks really uncomfortable.

c)
1 It must be true.   g) I'm sure it's true.
2 It can't be true.   h) I'm sure it isn't true.
3 It might be true.   e) I think it's possibly true.
4 It might not be true. f) I think it possibly isn't true.
5 It must have been true. c) I'm sure it was true.
6 It can't have been true. d) I'm sure it wasn't true.

7 It might have been true.   a) I think it was possibly true.
8 It might not have been true. b) I think it possibly wasn't true.

d)
1 can't have   2 might have
3 must have   4 can't have

7a) and b) 🎧 (53)
PHIL: Dawn, you've been there before. Do you think it's worth buying things at the famous Tei-Kyo-Mu-Ni market?
DAWN: Not really. They only sell rubbish which you don't really need. It isn't worth the money. And they try to overcharge you. It's a complete rip-off.
P: How about the famous and beautiful Wai-Yu-Hia hill? Is it worth trying to climb it?
D: No, not really. It's very tiring, and when you get to the top, all you can see is a giant nuclear power station. It's a real let-down. I don't think it's worth the energy, myself.
P: OK then. Is it worth visiting Em-Ti Square? Sophie told me that it's really impressive to look at.
D: No, let's not go there. The locals don't go near it at all. It's just a tourist trap. And it takes ages to get there. It's simply not worth the time.
P: Er … Dawn, *why* exactly *are* we going?
1 buying   2 money   3 rip-off
4 trying   5 let-down   6 energy
7 visiting   8 tourist trap 9 time

c)

Extreme	Less extreme
boiling	hot
terrific	good
beautiful	pretty
hilarious	funny
exhausting	tiring
enormous	big
terrible	bad

d) and e) 🎧 (54)
PHIL: The weather! It was absolutely boiling.
DAWN: Oh, come on. It wasn't that hot.
P: And I met this beautiful girl, Lai-Kyu.
D: I don't think she was that pretty!
P: She had an enormous pair of eyes!
D: They weren't that big. They were really piggy.
P: You're just jealous. She had a great sense of humour. She was absolutely hilarious!
D: Was she? I don't remember laughing. She wasn't that funny.
P: Anyway, I walked up Wai-Yu-Hia hill with her. It was exhausting!
D: It can't have been that tiring. You seemed to have lots of energy later in the evening.
P: Anyway, I had a terrific time.

D: It wasn't that good. I've had better holidays.

P: But Dawn was terrible company. She really got on my nerves.

D: Was I? I don't think I was that bad.

1 ... she was that pretty
2 ... weren't that big.
3 ... wasn't that funny.
4 ... that tiring.
5 ... wasn't that good.
6 ... I was that bad

8a) ●● (55)

GUIDE: And now, ladies and gentlemen, if you'll just follow me through the arch into the main arena ... here we are. Just look around you, ladies and gentlemen, and take in the ... the breathtaking majesty of it all. Just think, this was built two-and-a-half thousand years ago, before the people had access to modern tools and architectural expertise. As the sheer size of the arena suggests, this was a place where large crowds could congregate for a very specific purpose. It used to be thought that this was a sporting arena, where man would do battle against both man and beast. However, the latest theories and research now suggest that the square was, in fact, used for religious ceremonies.

TOURIST: Are you sure, madam?

G: Yes, quite sure. We can see over on the west side of the square, various enclosures. These enclosures are where the elders and the high priests of Magnesia would stand while the ceremony was carried out.

T: They look like animal enclosures to me.

G: I have it on good authority, sir, if you don't mind, that the square must have been used for religious ceremonies. There is no other rational explanation. Look, over there is the altar, where animals were killed to satisfy the gods.

T: But if you look at it again, those enclosures over there could have been for animals. Perhaps the Magnesians brought the animals through the arch, and put them over there to stop them from running away. People might have come here to buy and sell animals. And they might have sold other things here, too. Tomatoes, carrots, all manner of things.

G: But sir. Please take my word for it that this square was used for religious ceremonies.

T: Rubbish! It was a market-place. It's obvious!

G: Anyway, if you'll all come with me over to the altar...

T: Altar!

G: ...to ... the ... altar ... , I'll show you something which will prove the theory.

T: I can't wait.

FEMALE TOURIST: Jeremy, stop it. You're embarrassing me. Will you just listen to what the lady has to say. She must know what she's talking about. It's her job!

T: Well, she can't have been trained very well. It's obvious this was a market-place. It couldn't have been anything else.

FT: Why don't you wait outside. You're spoiling it for everyone.

T: No, er ... I'll ... er ... just ...

G: OK, ladies and gentlemen. Here it is. Fashioned from the horn of a cow, this was an instrument of beauty. The most beautiful women, the very cream of Magnesian beauty, used these to comb their hair in preparation for the ceremony.

T: What nonsense!

FT: Jeremy! Please!

T: No, let me have my say. May I ask you, why are you so confident that it was used for brushing women's hair?

G: Well, it's what I was told by Sir Arthur Expert. They must have been used for brushing women's hair, because there is no other rational explanation.

T: Yes there is ...

FT: Jeremy ... please ...

T: It's obvious. Nobody would brush their hair with that! It's got a pointed end. They'd do themselves an injury! Look. If this was a market-place, which I'm pretty certain it was ... then that thing there must have been used to poke the cows with, to make them go faster. Combing hair... I've never heard such rubbish in all my life. Call yourself a tour guide! You don't know anything!

FT: Come on Jeremy. We're going back to the hotel. Mrs Perkins, I'm ever so sorry for my husband's behaviour...

G: That's OK. Now, ladies and gentlemen, if you'll follow me over to the amphitheatre ...

T: It isn't an amphitheatre, it's a swimming pool!

FT: Shut up, Jeremy!

1 b)   2 b)   3 a)   4 b)   5 a)   6 b)

b) ●● (56)

FT: Honestly, Jeremy, I've never been so embarrassed in all my life! We've got to spend another ten days with all of those people. I won't know what to say to them!

T: Well, I ask you. She calls herself a tour guide.

FT: Will you just leave it? Your behaviour was ... was ... unforgivable. Totally out of order.

T: I don't see ... I don't see what I did wrong! I was just offering a different opinion.

FT: Offering a different opinion? You were just completely rude. There's no better word for it.

T: Well, honestly, £20 each we paid for that tour! £20 each! What a complete waste of money.

F: A waste of energy, yes. But only because you spoiled it for everyone. I was enjoying it until you started arguing with her. For years ... years ... I've wanted to see the ruins of Ancient Magnesia. I'll probably never get to come here again. Not on your salary, anyway.

T: Now, now, let's not get personal.

FT: You were pathetic today! I wouldn't expect that behaviour from a child.

T: Now come on. I wasn't that bad!

FT: Oh! It just isn't worth talking to you. This whole holiday is in ruins! I'm going to the bar, to talk to Dimitri ...

T: Suit yourself ...

1 b)   2 a)   3 b)   4 a)   5 c)

c)

1 The square must have been used for religious ceremonies.
2 They might have kept animals there.
3 The square can't have been used for religious ceremonies.
4 The people might have brought the animals through the arch.
5 People might have come here to buy and sell animals.
6 She can't have been trained very well for her job.
7 It must have been used for brushing women's hair.
8 It can't have been used for brushing hair.

Do you remember? Units 10–12

1

1 This wall was built by the Romans.
2 You can be arrested for pretending to be a police officer.
3 The football match was won by Tadchester City.

4 The winning goal was scored by Danny Beckenham.
5 Fewer computers are being bought these days.
6 At some point in the future, the earth is going to be hit by a large asteroid.
7 Millions of e-mails are sent every day.
8 Something should be done about it.

2
1 apologise
She apologised for arriving late.
I'm sorry for arriving late.
2 promise
He promised not to forget to phone her mother.
I won't forget to phone your mother.
3 warn
He warned her that another car was coming straight towards them.
Another car is coming straight towards us.
4 offer
She offered him a cup of coffee.
Do you want a cup of coffee?
5 refuse
The bank manager refused to lend him any more money.
I can't lend you any more money.
6 offer
He offered to drive.
Do you want me to drive?

3a) and b) ⊙⊙ (57)
MAN: It can't be modern. It's got an arm missing.
WOMAN: It can't have been made like that.
M: It might be representation of a powerless society.
W: It might have fallen off while they were bringing it to the museum.
M: Or the artist might have knocked it off accidentally.
W: Yes. He can't have been happy about that.
M: He might have made it like that.
W: It might not have been a man. It might have been a woman.
M: That could be a reason …
W: Another museum must have the arm.

Do you remember everything?
1 h	2 a	3 v	4 e
5 y	6 o	7 u	8 m
9 a	10 d	11 e	12 a
13 n	14 y	15 m	16 i
17 s	18 t	19 a	20 k
21 e	22 s		

The question made is:
Have you made any mistakes?

Extend your reading Units 10–12
1
1 Big Brother   2 nine weeks   3 ten
2
1 volunteer   2 contestant
3 voyeuristic   4 clash   5 eject
3
1 = T   2 = T   3 = F   4 = F   5 = T   6 = F
4
summary c)
5
1 d)   2 f)   3 a)   4 g)   5 c)
6 e)   7 b)
6 (Possible answers)
1 They had to live in Iron Age conditions.
2 Some of the children from *Living in the Past* will be in *Surviving the Iron Age*.
3 Because the BBC is a public service.
4 To get more viewers./ Because B*ig Brother* was very popular.
5 Ordinary people. / Members of the public.
6 They have to escape, either individually or together.
7 The first.
8 There are escape routes in the set.
9 Someone who escapes alone.
10 They can send in advice to the contestants.

Extend your grammar Units 10–12
1
1 however	2 by	3 who
4 so	5 can	6 flight
7 Although	8 were	9 making
10 involving	11 managed	12 Luckily
13 get	14 that	15 asked
16 to	17 must	18 do
19 taking	20 had	

2
1 They got arrested for reckless driving.
2 He was given a ten-year sentence.
3 They aren't allowed to go out on Sundays.
4 I finally succeeded in getting tickets for the film you wanted.
5 Unfortunately, I wasn't able to get the seats you wanted.
6 He refused to help us.
7 They agreed to come to the theatre with us.
8 He can't have been on that plane with you.

Extend your writing Units 10–12
1
There has always been violence in the world. (A)
More young people are violent now than before. (G)
Children have to learn other ways of solving their problems from their parents. (W)
It is better to understand violence than to ignore it. (A)

There is a link between watching violence on TV and an increase in aggression. (F and G)
It's not TV that makes you violent, some people are already like that. (A)
There are other things that children can do besides watching TV. (W)
2
1 on the other hand
2 The purpose of this report
3 Firstly
4 not only
5 but also
6 In addition
7 In contrast
8 moreover
9 and
10 Finally
11 In my opinion
12 as a result
13 not only
14 but also

Pearson Education Limited,
Edinburgh Gate
Harlow
Essex CM20 2JE
England
And Associated Companies throughout the World.

www.longman.com

First published 2001
Fifth impression 2006

Set in 11.5/13pt Bulldog

Printed in Malaysia, PPSB

ISBN-13: 978-0-582-43869-9
ISBN-10: 0-582-43869-1

Illustrated by: Matt Buckley, Phil Healey and Tim Kahane.
Cover illustration by Tim Kahane.

Acknowledgements

The publishers are most appreciative of the contribution of Ana Fraile and
Alejandro Zarzalejos as authors of the 'Extend your reading/grammar/writing'
pages in this Workbook and wish to thank them, and also Brigit Viney and
Lynne Rushton for their contribution to the development of these pages. The
publishers would also like to thank Liz Paren (freelance Editor) for her
contribution to the development of the manuscript of this Workbook.

Photo Acknowledgements

We are grateful to the following for permission to reproduce copyright
photographs:

BBC for all photos on 10; Andrew Crowley/Daily Telegraph for 62; Robert
Harding Picture Library for 9; Hulton Getty for 27; Kobal Collection for 32
and 74; Amit Lennon for 17; Pearson Education/Peter Lake for 47; Rex
Features for 36 both photos, 39 and 53; Rex Features/SIPA for 71; The
Stock Market for 14.

Freelance Picture Research by Liz Moore.

We are grateful to the following for permission to reproduce copyright
material:

BBC for an article based on *Westway*, a BBC World Service Radio Drama
series; Carlton Books for extracts adapted from "Model citizen" and "Hot
dish" by Yorick Brown and Mike Flynn, published in *The Best Book of
Urban Myths Ever*; the author's agent for an extract adapted from "The
Sound Machine" by Roald Dahl, published in *Someone Like You* by
Michael Joseph; The Irish Times for an extract from "Survey finds Dublin
hard on walker" by Mary Carolan, published in *The Irish Times* 1st
September 1998; Little, Brown & Company for an extract from *Don't say
'yes' when you want to say 'no'* by Herbert Fensterheim and Jean Bear;
Los Angeles Times Syndication International and Reader's Digest USA for
an extract from "Get career connected" by Gina Imperato, published in
Fast Company March 2000; News International Associated Services for an
extract adapted from "TV rivals follow big brother" by Paul McCann,
published in *The Times* 12th August 2000 © Paul McCann / Times
Newspapers Limited 2000; and Telegraph Group Limited for extracts
adapted from "Mobile mania spreads as phones become the must-have
gadget" by Robert Uhlig, published in *Daily Telegraph* 6th January 2000,
and "24-hour gameshow gives entrants no place to hide" by Tom
Leonard, published in *Daily Telegraph* 28th June 2000.

In some instances we have been unable to trace the owners of copyright
material, and would welcome any information that would enable us to do so.